THE BABOON

The Baboon

by Richard Gardner

THE MACMILLAN COMPANY,
NEW YORK, NEW YORK

The Macmillan Company,
866 Third Avenue, New York, N.Y. 10022
Collier-Macmillan Canada Ltd., Toronto, Ontario

Library of Congress catalog card number: 73-102963
Printed in the United States of America

10 9 8 7 6 5 4 3 2 1

CONTENTS

29774

Just as the baboon has had a share in man's history, he will have a share in man's future. He is a fellow primate and represents an important stage in man's evolutionary development. Like the earliest known man-apes, the baboon left the abundance and security of life in the trees to take up a more difficult life in the open. As a consequence, the baboon is one of the more aggressive and venturesome of the primates, probably second only to man. Like man, the baboon evolved into a highly social animal, and study of his social organization can offer us some interesting insights into our own social behavior. The baboon is physiologically similar to man in several important ways and is increasingly helpful in medical, scientific and industrial research. Last but not least, the baboon is a part of the earth's vast and infinitely complex natural system, which we must learn to understand and control with reason, lest we disrupt it entirely and destroy ourselves in the process.

1

THE DOG-HEADED GOD:
The Baboon in Legend and Myth

Until recently the baboon has had an unsavory reputation in the modern world, particularly in the Christian West. Baboons were said to be uncouth, unclean, and of no use. They were charged with being familiars of the devil, and tradition had it that they made love indiscriminately and around the clock.

Men have not always considered the baboon to be a buffoon and rogue. In ancient times the baboon was considered sacred, was trained as a priest and was consulted by Pharaohs. In fact, the baboon has long been regarded with sympathy and respect by many of the native peoples of Africa, one of the earliest centers of civilization.

The Bushmen, who roam South Africa's Kalahari

Chacma mother and child

Desert, have been close neighbors of baboons for as long as any other race of men, far longer than most. There is an old saying among them that in very ancient times in South Africa there were only Bushmen and baboons. Their ancestors probably revered baboons as sacred, and carved drawings of them into hard stone. Present-day Bushmen say that their ancestors handed down to them the ability to talk with baboons.

The Bushmen describe the baboon as "he who sits on his hands," meaning that the baboon is lazier than themselves. But they also respect the baboon for its strength, ferocity and intelligence. They think of it as a less fortunate relative, clever but immature, capricious and emotional.

Certain other ancient societies have also shown respect for the baboon, several considering the animal to be magical or sacred. But the ancient Egyptians were the only ones to actually elevate baboons to the priesthood.

They believed the baboon to be the sacred representative of Thoth, the god of wisdom and knowledge, who was sometimes depicted with the head of an ibis, sometimes with that of a baboon. Thoth was said to have invented the arts and sciences, including words and writing. According to one myth Thoth taught the baboon how to speak the secret language of the gods. According to another the baboon taught the god how to make the ancient Egyptian hieroglyphics. All the myths agreed that certain special baboons could read and write and could converse with the gods.

The species favored by the Egyptians was the hamadryas, which is native to the northeastern part of Africa and to southern Arabia. Like all baboons, the hamadryas has a dog-like face, with deeply set eyes and a long, squared muzzle. Like other baboons, the hamadryas travels and forages in a pack, or troop, and goes on all fours like a dog. But the hamadryas is stronger and more intelligent than a dog and can be far more deadly, with his muscular shoulders and saber-like canine teeth. The hamadryas' most striking feature is the cape of long brindled gray hair in the male, which gives him a distinguished, even regal appearance. With its habit of sitting solemnly with its hands on its knees, seemingly disdaining to look directly at others, the hamadryas has the aloof and distracted air of a high priest. It dominates its females, a characteristic which the Egyptians admired. They noticed that their captive baboons never missed a chance to bask in the morning sun and that they were often heard to bark sharply just as the sun appeared. It seemed to the Egyptians that the baboons worshiped the sun god, Ra, as they did. Seeing the hamadryas bark at the rising sun, they believed that the baboon greeted the sun god each morning and spoke to him in the special language of the gods.

For over three thousand years the baboon was one

of the most important animals in Egyptian religious life and art. The oldest known statue from the culture of the Nile is the alabaster figure of a baboon carved thirty-four hundred years before the birth of Christ. In tomb paintings, baboons were depicted with their hands raised in prayer and their mouths opened in songs of praise to the sun. Stone statues of baboons stood at the eastern entrances to temples, facing the rising sun. One of the four canopic jars in which the viscera of dead royalty were kept was always carved in the shape of a baboon. The baboon's hieroglyphic name 〔⟩⌐⌐〕 appears repeatedly in Egyptian texts. On one ancient papyrus scroll there is a drawing of a baboon, representing Thoth, healing the left eye of heaven, while behind the baboon a man bows down in supplication.

Worship of the sun reached its height around 2400 B.C., when Heliopolis was capital of Egypt and its patron, Ra, was the principal god. Since Thoth was considered to be Ra's scribe, the baboon was treated with particular reverence during that time. There were few if any hamadryas baboons native to the lower Nile, so they were imported from the kingdoms of the upper Nile. They were brought to Egypt by Phoenician traders and later by the ships of Solomon. Sometimes they were sent by lesser kings as tribute to the Pharaohs.

Newly arrived baboons were brought before the priests, presented with writing table, reed pen and ink, and invited to write. They were expected to write in the language of the gods. But of course only the priests could say if they succeeded. Those that failed the test were put to menial tasks, but those the priests approved were declared sacred and were given special tasks to perform in the temples. They were also given special privileges and special food, and when they died, they were honored with mummification. The mummies of tens of thousands of sacred baboons have been found, preserved in the seated position, with their individual names written in ink on the bands of cloth enclosing them.

The Egyptians divided their baboons into the same three classes into which they divided themselves. While the upper-class baboons enjoyed special privileges in the temples, lower-class baboons were required to slave for the aristocrats and others who could afford them. They were trained to perform an amazing variety of jobs in house and field. When the working-class baboon died, it was also given formal burial, but in the less costly manner reserved for the human poor.

All in all the baboon was probably more intimately a part of man's life during the thirty centuries of Egyptian civilization than any other animal before or since, the dog not excluded.

The Greeks adopted Thoth as their own god, calling him Hermes, but they dispensed with his mythical scribe, the sacred hamadryas, which they called *cyno-*

cephalus, meaning "dog-headed." They thought the baboon ugly because it did not have the round buttocks they so admired in themselves. Because they were so beautiful, they reasoned, the baboon, being different, had to be ugly.

The Muslims were equally contemptuous of the baboon and were reminded in their holy book, the Koran, of certain Jews who had been turned into monkeys as punishment for breaking the Sabbath. Both the Hebrews and Romans considered it bad luck to dream of baboons. During the Roman games staged by Pompey around 55 B.C., baboons were thrown into the arena to fight leopards and lions. But it was the Christians who decided that the baboon was not merely ugly but evil as well.

During antipagan riots in Alexandria in A.D. 391 all the temples of Thoth were destroyed by Christian rioters. Only one large statue of a sacred baboon was left standing, an example of the "hideous evil" that the pagans had worshiped. By the time of the Middle Ages Western Christianity had adopted the ape as a symbol of consummate lust and folly. In paintings, sculpture and manuscripts the baboon was represented, along with the goat, as the personification of the Evil One, Satan himself. As late as the early nineteenth century the baboon was still being described as having a devilish temper and a satanic sexual appetite. In 1802 the French naturalist Buffon wrote of a baboon he had seen in Ethiopia: "It was insolently lascivious, and satisfied its strong desires in public. It seemed also to make a parade of its nakedness, presenting its posterior oftener to the spectators than its head."

Opinions of the baboon as lewd and lustful were often based on observation of actual baboon behavior, but it was not necessarily natural behavior. Even normal behavior was usually misunderstood, as we shall see in the chapters ahead.

In the first known scientific description of the primate family, written around 350 B.C., the Greek philosopher Aristotle noted the similarity between monkeys and men: "Some animals share the properties of man and the quadruped, as the ape, the monkey, and the baboon. The monkey is a tailed ape. The baboon resembles the ape in form, only that it is bigger and stronger, more like a dog in face, and is more savage in its habits, and its teeth are more dog-like and more powerful."

By baboon, Aristotle probably meant the sacred hamadryas of Egypt. The early Greeks didn't know much about the other species of baboon, and they knew virtually nothing about the anthropoid apes: the gibbon, the chimpanzee, orangutan and gorilla.

The first dissections of baboons were made by the Greek physician-physiologist Galen around A.D. 160. After studying the cadavers of dozens of baboons and other monkeys, he reported that "of all living things, the ape is likest man in viscera, muscles, arteries, veins and nerves, as in the form of the bones."

But after Galen, scientific study of the primates was virtually dropped for fifteen hundred years. Medieval scholars, mostly churchmen, were primarily interested in abstract speculation. The ape, they decided, was a debased form of human being, a fallen man, just as men were supposed to be fallen angels. If a pregnant woman looked an ape in the eye, they said, her child would be born a baboon. One medieval writer, Bartholomew of England, did observe that monkeys had a habit of picking through one another's fur. But he considered this grooming activity to be a bad habit and concluded that "the ape is a monstrous beast that delights in picking and eating vermin and everything else unclean."

With the dawning of the Renaissance, men renewed their interest in the world around them and returned to scientific study of both dead and living animals. Eventually, in 1758, Linnaeus described and classified all the known animals, lumping men, apes and the sloth together in one order which he called *Anthropomorpha*.

But most people, scientists included, were not ready to accept so close a relationship between monkeys and men. The Frenchman Buffon published a scientific account of the gibbon and was equally fascinated by the orangutan, but he was careful to insist that the human qualities of the great apes had been exaggerated. The dog and the elephant, he said, were closer to man in intelligence and temperament than any of the primates.

And then, in 1859, a biologist named Charles Darwin shocked Victorian England by publishing a revolutionary scientific argument supporting the hypothesis that men and primates were close cousins.

Darwin did not actually say in *Origin of Species* that man was descended from the monkeys. But his theory of evolution through natural selection held that living creatures changed gradually, from generation to generation, over long periods of years. Man had not been created overnight and complete only five thousand years before, as most churchmen claimed. Man had evolved slowly, over millions of years, from ancestors which he held in common with the modern monkeys and apes.

The theory was fiercely attacked by churchmen, scientists and such statesmen as Benjamin Disraeli, who declared: "The question is this: is man an ape or an angel? My Lord, I am on the side of the angels."

Such criticism was extreme. Darwin had not said that men and apes were identical, but only that they had a *common ancestry* and were therefore similar to some degree. But he had pricked the pride of mankind. Men had long believed that they were unique and

Nineteenth century painting by George Stubbs, A Drill and
Albino Baboon (*by kind permission of the President and
Council of the Royal College of Surgeons of England*)

Ancient statue of baboon
female and children, and
experimental animals at
the Southwest Founda-
tion for Research
and Education

specially created by God, and they were not likely to
give up that satisfying idea without a fight.

Scientists were the first to accept the theory of evolution through natural selection. Thomas Huxley used
Darwin's work to support his thesis that man should be
included in the same family as the primates. Ernest
Haeckel was the first scientist to actually draw an evolutionary tree showing man's close relationship to the
anthropoid monkeys and apes, including the baboon.

One beneficial result of the evolution controversy

was the stimulation of scientific and public interest in the primates. Apes and monkeys became the most popular exhibits in circuses and zoos. Through the turn of the century several pioneer attempts were made to study monkeys in the wild, but not much accurate information resulted. In 1928 an anatomist named Solly Zuckerman began his important study of the social activities of the hamadryas colony in the London Zoo. Through the next two decades, the study of primates, often in their wild state, was carried forward by a select number of dedicated men, among them C. R. Carpenter, Robert M. Yerkes, Henry Nissen, and Harold C. Bingham. Finally, beginning in the early 1950s, the study of primates began to attract favorable public attention. Scientists received increased financial support for their work, and new studies were undertaken by such researchers as S. L. Washburn, K. R. L. Hall, Hans Kummer, J. H. Crook, Irven DeVore, and Jane van Lawick-Goodall. Slowly a picture is emerging of the myriad primate colonies and communities, many of them very much like our own prehistoric ancestors in fundamental needs and behavior.

2

COMMON ANCESTORS:
The Baboon in Evolution

Both man and the baboon have evolved from a common ancestor—a furry insect eater no bigger than a rat, which began its existence as one of the first primates some eighty million years ago. The primate family of animals presently includes the suborder Anthropoidea —monkeys, apes and man—as well as the suborder prosimians. But eighty million years ago there were neither monkeys, apes nor men, but only the prosimians—the half-monkeys or pre-monkeys.

Among the prosimians living today is the tiny tree shrew of Malaysia. Although no fossil remains of the first prosimian primates have been identified, most paleontologists agree that the creatures were probably very much like this tree shrew. At first glance the tree shrew looks like a small pink-nosed rodent with a furry tail. But it has certain characteristics which make it more monkey-like. It spends most of its time in the trees, and it is quick and agile, using its tail for balance and grasping branches with the jointed fingers of a primitive hand.

The one thing the primates all have in common is that until recently they were forest-dwelling animals. Some baboons, a few other species of monkey and man have come down from the trees to take up life on the open plain. Although the savanna baboon, the most numerous subspecies, spends most of its day on the ground, it usually returns to the trees at night. South African chacma baboons sleep atop high heaps of rock when trees are not available. Even the hamadryas and gelada baboons, which inhabit barren and treeless lands, retreat at night to the highest place they can find, usually a rocky cliff or escarpment. Because all primates were originally tree dwellers, they share the ability to climb by grasping. Nonprimates such as squirrels and cats must dig in with their claws. But it is much safer and more efficient to wrap jointed fingers around branches and proceed "hand over hand" as monkeys do. Those creatures with the most efficient hands tended to survive in the trees more readily than those without. The tree shrew was probably one of the first animals to develop a hand that could grasp branches and food objects.

Life in the trees required other adaptations. Ground dwellers depend heavily on their sense of smell to guide them through thick jungle or deep grass and to help them find their food, especially at night. But visibility is generally better up in the trees, and scent does not linger as long there as it does on the ground. Good eyesight is far more useful for hunting food in the trees than is an acute sense of smell. The ability to judge by sight the distance between branches is essential to the safety of an animal that climbs or swings far above the ground. Consequently, those pre-monkeys with improved vision had a better chance to survive.

The tree shrew possessed some of the basic adaptations demanded by arboreal life. In addition to its primitive hand, its eyes were relatively large. And they were surrounded by bony rings, the beginning of the enclosed eye sockets common to all monkeys and necessary for protection and support of more complex eyes.

Sometime toward the beginning of the Oligocene period, thirty-six million years ago, some of the prosimians began to fade toward almost total extinction. Today they remain only as evolutionary relics in certain isolated areas, such as the island of Madagascar off the eastern coast of Africa, where they do not have to compete directly with either their more advanced cousins, the anthropoids, or monkeys, or with the modern carnivores.

Fossils of the earliest monkeys are scarce. But most experts agree that of all the living prosimians, the tarsier comes closest to resembling the first common ancestor of nonhuman primates and man. There were once at least twenty-five varieties of tarsier spread throughout the Old World and the Americas. Today there is only one, living on a small island in the East Indies. He represents, after the tree shrew, the next major step in the evolution of the prosimians.

The modern tarsier is about the size of a chipmunk, with short arms and very long kangaroo-like legs. It is nocturnal, that is, it is most active at night. Its eyes are enormous, the largest in proportion to its body of any other primate, making the little animal's face look more like that of an owl than a monkey.

It possesses a number of characteristics that are more monkey-like than prosimian. Its hands and feet are very efficient, with long, nailed fingers that have bulging pads on the ends to aid in grasping. Its eye sockets are set close together at the front of its head and have protective walls of bone at the back. The part of its brain devoted to vision is relatively large. Its nose is dry and its snout blunt. It sits upright and is able to swivel its head 180 degrees, so that it can look directly behind itself without changing position.

In evolving from the prosimians, the first monkeys carried the basic primate characteristics further than the tarsier. Claws became for the most part a thing of the past. In some forms the hand developed an opposable thumb that could exert force against the fingers, insuring a firm grip. As the hand's sense of touch continued to improve, the surface of the nose became less sensitive, tougher and drier. As the eyes became permanently located in the front, the snout grew smaller and shrank back against the skull, creating the relatively flat "face" common to most anthropoids. As the eyes and hand improved, so did skill at judging distance and grasping and manipulating objects. Food could be plucked and lifted to the mouth with the hands rather than searched out on the ground with the probing snout. In these and other ways the primate's body became more efficient.

As the skeletal and muscular systems improved, the brain kept pace, step by step. As more and more dependence was placed on the hands, the area of the brain devoted to their control became larger and more complex. As the sense of smell became less important, the area of the brain mediating that sense decreased in size. As the mechanism of the eye continued to improve and more dependence was placed on vision, the area of the brain controlling vision grew larger and more complex.

By the end of the Oligocene period, three main characteristics distinguished the anthropoid primates from the other mammals. They had efficient hands, improved eyesight, and more highly developed brains.

CENOZOIC ERA

The geological era in which mammals first appeared

Period		Epoch	Years Ago
Paleogene	Tertiary	Paleocene	70,000,000–60,000,000
		Eocene	60,000,000–40,000,000
		Oligocene	40,000,000–25,000,000
Neogene		Miocene	25,000,000–10,000,000
		Pliocene	10,000,000–1,000,000
Quarternary		Pleistocene	1,000,000–10,000
		Recent	10,000–present

During the Miocene age that followed, the more immediate ancestors of the modern monkeys and apes began to appear. The Miocene began about twenty-five million years ago and is known as the Golden Age of Mammals. It was a time of favorable weather. The polar icecaps had receded, the seas were warm, and the earth was girdled in verdant tropical forests. Mastodons and saber-toothed tigers roamed the jungles and savannas, while most of the monkeys kept to the forest where food was abundant.

It was a perfect time for tree dwellers, and the anthropoids increased rapidly in number and variety, developing along separate but parallel lines in the Old World and the New.

In the Americas the tiny marmosets were the first to evolve from the original prosimian stock. After them came the squirrel monkeys, capuchins, howlers, woolly monkeys and spider monkeys. Eventually some sixty-five species of New World monkey evolved, in great variety of shape and color. But neither the baboon nor the great ape ever appeared in the New World.

The first monkeys to appear in Africa and Asia were the ancestors of today's common guenons and mangabeys. The langurs and colobus monkeys developed specialized stomachs with enabled them to digest leaves and fibrous materials. Eventually some fifty-eight species of Old World monkey appeared in Europe, Africa and Asia.

It was also in the Old World, probably in Central Africa, that in Miocene times the first baboons appeared and, along with them, the first anthropoid apes, the ancestors of the modern great apes and man.

The fossil record of primate evolution is far from complete. The ground-dwelling mammals sometimes died in the mud at the edge of water holes or tarpits, where their bones were likely to be preserved for examination by later scientists. But the primates most often died in the dense forests, their bodies falling to the ground and quickly decomposing, leaving no trace behind. Much of the primate record must be deduced from what few fossils have been found in Asia and Africa, from what we know of past weather and environmental conditions and from examination of living forms and study of their habits.

Some experts think that the anthropoid apes and the Old World monkeys, including the baboon, evolved in two separate and distinct lines. But we cannot be sure when the lines diverged. The baboon and the great apes may have parted evolutionary company at the time of the ancient tarsiers or at a much later date. It may be that the ancestors of the baboons and other large Old World monkeys did not separate from those of the apes back in the time of the tarsier, but more recently in the favorable Miocene. At any rate, as the Miocene came to an end, the anthropoids inhabited the forests in the New World, from Southern Mexico to the southernmost tip of South America; and in the Old World, from Central Europe to South Africa and from Central China to the southernmost islands of Malaysia.

And then, with the beginning of the Pliocene age, around ten million years ago, the weather began to change. Rainfall lessened and a great drought covered the earth. The savannas and deserts spread and the forests shrank, leaving fewer and fewer trees for the fast-growing populations of nonhuman primates. For many of them, either crowded out of the trees or seeking wider ranges and a more varied diet, there was no place to go but back to the ground.

Terrestrial, or ground-dwelling, apes and monkeys

had appeared long before the end of the Miocene, but it was during the harder times of the Pliocene that they began to emerge fully developed. Those already equipped to deal with the difficulties of life in the open survived; others less well prepared perished, some of starvation or disease, others falling to the predators which ruled the open spaces.

Ecology is a branch of biology that deals with the relation of living things to their environment and to each other. The ecology of an animal includes the physical context in which that animal lives and develops, and therefore includes such considerations as terrain, climate and food supply. Ecological factors influence change in the animal, physical and social, short term and long term. Among the important ecological influences on the physical and social evolution of both the early baboons and the first man-apes was the threat from predators, diseases and parasites. From its former tree-dwelling existence the baboon retained and perfected its dexterous hands and feet and its keen eyesight. It became heavier and stronger, and as a consequence lost much of its former grace and agility in the trees. But it made up for its losses in gains which made it better able to resist predators. The male baboon eventually evolved into a powerfully built fighting animal with massive shoulder muscles and a cowl of heavy fur, which served to protect the jugular vein and could be erected to give a frightening impression. The canine teeth grew larger. In order to support the larger teeth, the snout grew larger and longer. For a time, there were baboons larger than those of today. There are Pliocene fossils of baboons that equaled the size of gorillas.

The gradual shift from forest to open country also encouraged important changes in social organization. Out in the open, numbers were an advantage, not only for self-defense, but in the locating and gathering of food. The ground-dwelling primates had to learn to live and forage with one another in loosely organized bands or troops. Certain subgenera of baboon such as the hamadryas and gelada eventually migrated to even harsher and more exposed territories, where such eco-logical factors as periodic drought, shortage of food and relative absence of predator threat brought further modifications in their social organization.

The first man-apes also underwent drastic physi-cal and social changes while evolving from tree dwell-ers to ground dwellers. Probably in the beginning they also developed long canine teeth and may even have developed claws. But eventually they met their new ecological conditions with a far more revolutionary physical adaptation: bipedalism. The man-apes learned to walk and then to run upright. Standing and moving on only two feet left their hands free for feeding, skin care and fighting, and eventually for using tools and weapons.

By the Pleistocene age, between one and two million years ago, there were man-apes that walked upright and used simple tools and weapons. Fossilized remains of such creatures were first found by an anatomist named Raymond A. Dart in 1924. He named his "find" *Australopithecus africanus*, or the South African ape, and concluded that the man-ape had been only four feet tall and had weighed no more than ninety pounds. Mingled with the bones of *Australopithecus* were baboon skulls, some of which were fractured by what could only have been the blow of a weapon. Raymond Dart did not have to look far for the weapons that had crushed the baboon skulls, for among the bones of *Australopithecus* were a large number of antelope humeri, or upper foreleg bones. The heavy double-knobbed ends of these leg bones exactly fitted the double depression found in the fractured baboon skulls.

During the Pleistocene the man-apes became nomads, gathered together in loosely organized bands for mutual protection, hunting for what food they could pluck from the trees or dig from the earth or catch with their hands. They fled in terror from any animal larger or stronger than themselves.

Then as now, and for the same reasons, baboons also traveled and foraged in loosely organized social groups, called troops. Because the man-apes and the baboons were more or less evenly matched and were competing on the same ground for the same food, they

The prosimians from which the primates of today are descended seem to have looked very much like the tree shrew, above; of all the living prosimians, the tarsier, below, probably has the closest resemblance to the first common ancestor of nonhuman primates and man.

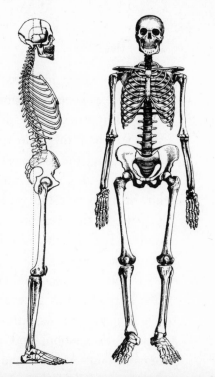

Skeletal structure of man and baboon: the baboon's skeleton is plantigrade—with the weight of the body placed on the heels of the hands and on the hind feet. The baboon is far behind the apes in the progression to the upright posture of man. (Courtesy of the American Museum of Natural History)

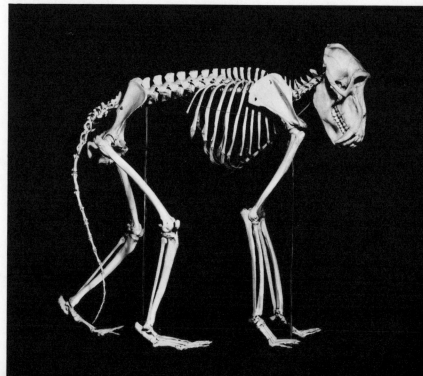

must have come into frequent conflict. In the beginning, the baboons probably won the battles, for they were equipped with deadly eye teeth and were much stronger than the man-apes. But the moment came when one of the man-apes plucked up an antelope leg bone, took aim and swung. We do not know exactly how it happened, but evidence indicates that the effective use of the weapon marks the beginning of man's million year ascent toward the nearly total supremacy which he enjoys today.

And the baboon, along with the anthropoid apes, was left behind as an evolutionary model of that time when man had recently developed upright posture, bipedal locomotion, and rudimentary forms of social organization. At that time man was also beginning to develop speech and was just on the verge of learning to use simple weapons and tools.

3

PAPIO:
Baboon Species, Range and Physical Characteristics

Baboons come in a variety of shapes, sizes and colors, and are known by a large number of names. The word baboon itself comes from the Medieval French *babouin*, or *babine*, which in turn comes from the word for lip, and probably derives from the baboon's habit of smacking the lips to signal peaceful intentions and greetings. In Middle English the word became *baboyne, babewyn*, and eventually, in modern English, baboon.

Baboon is a popular, not a scientific term, but it is useful as a generic name for one of the two major branches of the primate tree known as the Cynopithecoids, Cynocephaloids or "dog-headed" monkeys. The Cynopithecoids are the most diverse and most numer-

TAXONOMY OF THE BABOON

Superorder:	Neo Hominidae		
Order:	Primates		
Suborder:	Simiae (monkeys)		
Infraorder:	Catarrhini: (Old World monkeys)		
Family:	Cynopithecoids or Cercopithecoidae (dog-headed monkeys)		
Subfamily:	Cercopithecinae		

Genus	Subgenus	Species	Subspecies
A. Mangabeys			
(Cercocebus)	(1) Peaked (aterrimus)	1	1
	(2) Crested (albigena)	1	3
	(3) Capped (torquatus)	1	3
	(4) Plain-headed (galeritus)	1	3
B. Macaques			
(Macaca)	(1) Wanderoo (silenus)	1	1
	(2) Bonnet (radiata)	2	5
	(3) Crab-eating (irus)	1	21
	(4) Rhesus (rhesus mulatta)	3	7
	(5) Pig-tailed (nemestrina)	1	5
	(6) Stump-tailed (lyssodes)	2	7
	(7) Moor (magnus)	1	3
	(8) Barbary ape (simia)	1	1
	(9) Black ape (cynopithecus-cynoNiger)	1	1
C. Baboons			
(Papio)	(1) Drills (mandrillus)	2	2
	a) Mandrill (sphinx)		
	b) Drill (leocophaeus)		
	(2) Common or savanna baboons	4	18
	(2) Chacma (usinus or porcarius)		
	(3) Yellow (synocephalus)		
	(4) Anubis (doguera)		
	(5) Olive (papio)		
	(3) Hamadryas (hamadryas)	1	1
	(4) Gelada (theropithecus gelada)	1	1

ous of about eleven families of existing primates. They are more widely distributed across the earth's surface than any other group of primates with the exception of man. They can be found in forests and on mountains, on desert and grassy plain, from southernmost Africa to northern Honshu in Japan, from Gibraltar eastward all the way to Java, Borneo and the Celebes Islands. They are not found in the New World.

The Cynopithecoids are classified as monkeys. Taxonomists (scientists concerned with classification of animals) place them under the infraorder *Catarrhini* (Old World monkeys), under the suborder *Simiae* (monkeys), which is under the order Primates. The complete formal taxonomy of the baboon is on the opposite page.

There are two main branches of Cynopithecoids. One branch contains the true baboons. The other includes several species of smaller monkeys, less terrestrial than the true baboons, somewhat less aggressive, but nonetheless more baboon-like than other species of monkey. These are the mangabeys and macaques.

The mangabeys are small, retiring creatures which can be distinguished as members of the dog-headed family mainly by certain features of their skulls and teeth. They are the least baboon-like of the Cynopithecoids.

The macaques are the best known of all monkeys because of the extensive use of the rhesus in medical research. Other macaques are the wanderoo of India, the bonnet, stump-tailed, pig-tailed and crab-eating macaques, the red-faced monkeys of western China, and the Japanese macaque. Finally, there is the *magot*, or Barbary ape, even more baboon-like than the others, found on the Rock of Gibraltar and along the coast of North Africa.

All are hardy, tough, intelligent and aggressive. They travel on all fours, climb by grasping with hands and feet, are compactly and strongly built, and have formidable canine teeth. They live in troops, groups or communities, can maintain life on a wide variety of plants and fruits, and generally have physical and social traits similar to the baboon's. However, they are smaller and are not quite so much at home on the open plain as their adventuresome cousins the true baboons.

Since Aristotle's time there has been confusion over the naming and classification of primates, and modern taxonomists are still unable to agree on which species should be named what and in what order the various species should be listed. We have separated the mangabeys and macaques from those which we call the baboons. Taxonomists agree that the baboons should be included under the genus *Papio*, but they do not agree on the subgenera. We have had to make our own list, combining various of the best considered opinions. Under *Papio* we list these four subgenera:

The drills—West Coast of Africa
The common, or savanna, baboons—Central Africa
The hamadryas—Northeast Africa
The gelada—Ethiopia

The true baboons are not quite as wide ranging as the mangabeys and macaques. They are found exclusively in Africa and a small portion of Arabia. Although some species inhabit the jungles and some roam the seashore, the largest number of true baboons is found outside the closed canopy forests, usually in the open woodlands, on the flat savanna and in the dry, rocky uplands.

Only an expert can tell the difference between the skinned carcasses of the various species of true baboon, and except for their color, newborn infants look almost identical. They have heavy, hunched shoulders and a large head. That is because the animal is built to move and fight on the ground, not in the trees. Its frame is compact and its bones heavy. The arms are slightly longer than the legs, so that the backbone slopes backward from the head when the animal walks or runs. The skeleton is plantigrade, that is, the weight of the body usually rests on the heels of the hands and on the hind feet. However, the skeleton is so constructed as to enable the animal to sit fully upright, leaving the hands free. The baboon can stand on its hind feet for brief periods. Comparison of primate skeletons places the baboon far behind the apes, especially the gibbon, in progression toward the permanently upright posture of man.

The head is large, thrusting forward into a long muzzle with the nostrils at the tip. There are thirty-two permanent teeth, including incisors very much like a man's, exceptionally long canines and well-developed molars designed for the constant grinding required by a vegetable diet. The eyes are small, closely set and sunken, beneath a curved brow ridge so deep that the animal tilts its head back in order to look upward. The deep brow ridge probably protects the eyes, both from injuries during fighting and from the strong sunlight common to much of the baboon's range. The eyes are brownish yellow to chestnut in color and are exceptionally efficient; the baboon has better eyesight than most other primates. The eyes produce both color and stereoscopic vision.

Most of the face is hairless and may be black, pink or multicolored. The chin is usually bearded and the face framed by cheek ruffs. All true baboons have two cheek pouches, in each of which a good fistful of food can be stored. The head often has a topknot of hair which can be erected in excitement or as a threat. White eyelids, blinked rapidly, add to the threat display.

The hands and feet are well developed, and are almost as efficient as those of the apes, and may be gray or black. The tail may be only a stump or it may be over a foot long. It is never prehensile and has only limited use as a balancing aid in climbing. There are pads of thick flesh, called ischial callosities, on the animal's backside. These serve as cushions to help the baboon brace itself for sleeping in the crotches of trees or in rock crannies. The buttocks of both males and females range in color from dull pink to vivid scarlet.

There is usually a heavy growth of hair on the shoulders, longer in some species than others, and longer in males than females. The coat is thick and often brindled, ranging in color from yellow-green to charcoal, but most commonly a dull yellow-brown.

The baboon has a higher metabolic rate than man but a comparable heart rate. Much of the baboon's internal functioning and many of its internal organs have close similarities to those of man. The baboon's digestive system, like man's, is capable of processing a wide variety of foods.

Adult height varies from 18 inches seated to nearly three feet seated, with the average male measuring about 26 inches seated. Adult weight varies from 20 to 100 pounds, with the average male weighing about 60 pounds, the average female about 25. The well-muscled body has tremendous strength, particularly in the shoulders.

The true baboons conform to the above general physical characteristics. We have divided these true baboons into the following subgenera, separating them mostly on the basis of variations in coloring, size and form. However, they also vary in their social habits and organization, as we shall see in the next chapter.

The Drills

The drill and mandrill are among the most unusual-looking of the baboons. Both have the long thrusting muzzle common to all baboons. They have compact well-muscled bodies with small thick tails, which stand erect. They move with the typical baboon gait, stalking along with shoulders hunched and head swiveling left and right. The backbone slopes downward from head to rump when they walk; the large, hairless buttocks are pink to watermelon red in color. Compared to the males, the adult females of both species are small and modestly colored. Both have cheek ruffs and beards. The female drill is dull olive-brown in color. The female mandrill is charcoal-gray tinged with greenish brown.

The male drill is nearly two to three times the size of the female and has a pointed goatee at the end of its muzzle. Its face is a shiny jet-black and is surrounded by a deep fringe of hair which rises into a bristling crest atop the head.

The adult male mandrill is conspicuously colored. Under the gray fur its skin is bluish black, turning to

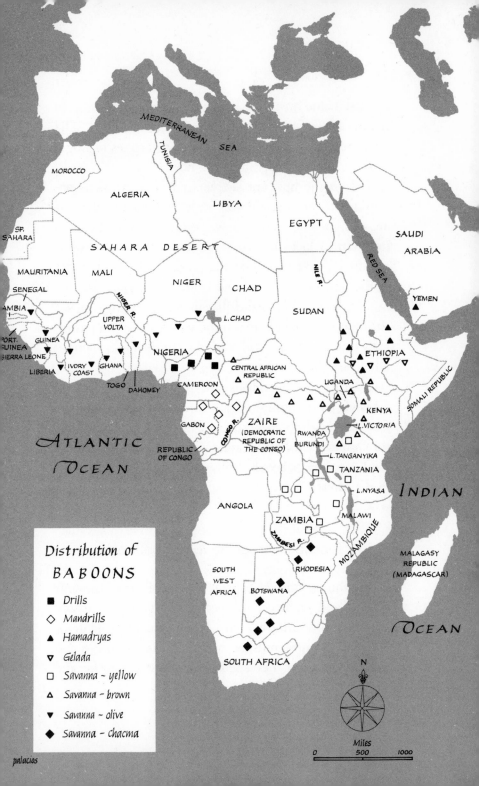

MEDITERRANEAN SEA

MOROCCO
TUNISIA
ALGERIA
LIBYA
EGYPT
SP. SAHARA
SAUDI ARABIA
MAURITANIA
MALI
NIGER
CHAD
SUDAN
RED SEA
NILE R.
YEMEN
SENEGAL
AMBIA
PORT. GUINEA
GUINEA
SIERRA LEONE
LIBERIA
IVORY COAST
GHANA
TOGO
DAHOMEY
NIGER R.
UPPER VOLTA
L. CHAD
NIGERIA
CAMEROON
CENTRAL AFRICAN REPUBLIC
ETHIOPIA
UGANDA
SOMALI REPUBLIC
KENYA
GABON
CONGO R.
ZAIRE (DEMOCRATIC REPUBLIC OF THE CONGO)
REPUBLIC OF CONGO
RWANDA
BURUNDI
L. VICTORIA
L. TANGANYIKA
TANZANIA
L. NYASA
ANGOLA
ZAMBIA
ZAMBESI R.
MALAWI
MOZAMBIQUE
RHODESIA
SOUTH WEST AFRICA
BOTSWANA
MALAGASY REPUBLIC (MADAGASCAR)
SOUTH AFRICA

ATLANTIC OCEAN
INDIAN OCEAN

Distribution of BABOONS

■ Drills
◇ Mandrills
▲ Hamadryas
▽ Gelada
□ Savanna – yellow
△ Savanna – brown
▼ Savanna – olive
◆ Savanna – chacma

N

Miles
0   500   1000

palacios

vivid sky-blue on the muzzle. There is nothing else in nature to compare with the face of the mandrill. The blue muzzle is marked by several long creases or ridges running down either side. The nose ridge and nostrils, and often the lips, are lacquer red. The whiskers are pure white, but the pointed beard and parts of the ruff are orange. The animal is as spectacular behind as it is in front; in fact, the color pattern of face and nose is repeated almost exactly in the purplish-blue and scarlet of the buttocks and the vivid violet of the genitals.

A large adult mandrill can top thirty-two inches sitting up and weigh up to ninety pounds. It is a powerfully built animal, and can do considerable damage when in a fighting mood.

Drills and mandrills are found in two limited areas of West Central Africa between Nigeria and the Congos; the drills in northern Cameroon, the mandrills throughout southern Cameroon and Gabon. Unlike most savanna baboons, drills and mandrills live deep in the forest.

The Common or Savanna Baboons

By far the majority of baboons are members of the four species and eighteen subspecies of common baboon. They are found throughout Africa, usually in more or less open country, outside the closed canopy forests and jungles. Because they spend their lives on rocky and

grassy plains, some experts call them the savanna baboons. All have bodies that generally conform to the
classic baboon form, with well-furred tails over a foot
long, that are carried high, arching upward and falling
not quite to the ground behind.

The chacma (*Papio ursinus*) is the largest of the
common baboons, and takes its popular name from the
Bushman's word for baboon, "t-chac-kamma." It has a
black face, hands and feet and a brindled coat of the
usual olive-green yellow-brown baboon color. It is
known as the southern savanna species and inhabits
the dry open areas of South Africa, Botswana and
parts of southern Rhodesia. Because it is often found
in the rocky upland, some experts classify it separately
from the other savanna baboons.

The yellow savanna baboon (*Papio cynocephalus*)
is smaller and usually more yellowish than the chacma.
It ranges north from Zambia to Tanzania and west to
southern Zaire (the Congo), and might be called the
Eastern savanna species.

The anubis (*Papio doguera*), sometimes called
the brown or Atbara baboon, has a pink face with a
coat that varies considerably in shades of yellow-brown.
It might be called the central species, ranging from
northern Tanzania all the way up to Ethiopia and
across the continent through Uganda almost to Lake
Chad. Hans Kummer has observed that in some of the
western parts of Ethiopia, the anubis territories overlap with those of the hamadryas and that the bound-

aries seem to be changing gradually. Other anubis live in forested regions of northeastern and central Africa and are referred to as tree-dwelling anubis. Like the drills and mandrills, they spend most of the day foraging on the ground, but retire to the trees at night.

The olive baboon (*Papio papio*) is known as the western species and is olive-brown in color. It is found up and down the Atlantic coast, from the Sahara south to the equatorial forest belt and as far inland as Lake Chad.

All four species of savanna baboon are much alike, and their territories overlap in several places. More than once a lone member of one savanna species has been accepted into a troop of another species. Hans Kummer reports that the hamadryas and anubis appear to interbreed, and Russian scientists have succeeded in mating a rhesus macaque with a hamadryas baboon, with fertile offspring resulting.

The Hamadryas

The sacred baboon of ancient Egypt is larger than the average savanna baboon, with the adult males measuring up to four feet tall when standing erect, over two and a half when sitting, and weighing up to ninety pounds. In eastern Ethiopia the hamadryas male is usually pale stone-gray or yellowish in color, with a pink face, and is distinguished by the wide ruff of hair standing out from each cheek. Like the gelada (see below), the hamadryas usually has a cape of long hair hanging down its shoulders. Kummer has noted that in western Ethiopia the hamadryas tends to have a darker, reddish skin and brown hair, possibly as a result of interbreeding with the neighboring Ethiopian anubis. The female hamadryas does not have so heavy a shoulder cape and is about half the size of the male.

In the ancient Ethiopian language the hamadryas is called *tot* or *tota*, after the Egyptian god Thoth. Its popular English name is taken from that of a mythical wood nymph, the hamadryad (from the Greek *hama*, "living together"; *drys*, "trees"). Despite the name, the hamadryas does not live in woodland, but in the treeless, dry, rocky backlands of the eastern Sudan and Ethiopia, and in the deserts of southwestern Arabia (Yemen). For this reason, it is sometimes known as the desert baboon.

The Gelada

The gelada is nearly as unusual in form and coloring as the mandrill. Like the hamadryas, the male gelada has a thick mane, but the hair of the cape is blacker, longer and thicker, almost reaching the ground when the baboon is seated. The tail is long and thick, end-

Left: at the top, a drill, and at the bottom, a mandrill male.
Below: a chacma family group

*Above: male savanna baboon at the Southwest Foundation.
Right: hamadryas family—the male distinguished by his thick
shoulder cowl*

Gelada female and child

The gelada has a distinctive pink to red area on the chest; the male, above, is distinguished by a thick cape of hair.

ing in an ovoid-shaped tuft of longer hairs. The muzzle is long but bulbous instead of pointed, dished inward and furrowed by ridges running its length. The face is grayish red and hairless. It is capable of a great range of expression, including the ability to turn the upper lip inside out and expose the teeth and most of the upper gums. The eyelids are stark white and flash rapidly when an animal is agitated and possibly signaling others. The chest is hairless in the center, exposing a heart-shaped area of flesh-pink to red.

The male gelada is large, weighing on the average about forty-five pounds, with a rare specimen having been weighed at nearly one hundred pounds. The male is twice the size of the female. Its teeth are the most formidable among the baboons, the canines growing as long as two and a half inches, longer than those of a full-grown lion.

The gelada's range covers the mountain regions of southern Ethiopia and overlaps the territory of the hamadryas at the lower altitudes. The two species sometimes join together during the day to feed, but they separate at night. The hamadryas appear to dominate the geladas and sometimes invade their territory, but in general the hamadryas keep to the lower altitudes, while the geladas are better adapted to the higher altitudes, where they feed and sleep along the edges of the towering cliffs and rugged escarpments of the highlands.

4

THE TROOP:
Social Behavior of the Baboon

The average baboon spends all its life within a few feet of other baboons. In fact, it has been well said that a baboon separated from its fellows is soon a dead baboon. All primates, including man, are gregarious and need the company and protection of others of their kind. Certain other animals, in particular the great predators, are able to roam alone for days, weeks, even months. Few primates are able to remain out of sight of their fellows for more than a few hours.

The size and characteristics of primate social groupings vary considerably. Gibbons travel and forage in small family groups, and squirrel monkeys live in large organized bands. Baboons live and forage in small family groups, but these also organize into larger groups or troops.

The exact forms of baboon social organization vary among the species. The social unit common to all species is the troop, but the size and stability of the troop varies, depending on the ecological conditions, including population pressures, faced by the particular species.

Among the savanna baboons, the troop numbers from 10 to 200 members, with the average troop numbering about 50. The savanna troop is relatively stable. Most members are born, live, and die within the same troop. The savanna troop stays together during the day and sleeps together at night. Members of one savanna troop very rarely leave their troop to join another. And the troops seldom mingle or combine.

Social organization is somewhat different among the hamadryas of the Ethiopian desert. The hamadryas troop is not so stable as that of the savanna baboons, and comes together mostly at night. For this reason, Kummer has called the hamadryas troop the "sleeping society." It can consist of from 12 to 750 animals, depending on the availability of food and sleeping places.

The gelada troop changes form during the day and also comes together most often at night, although geladas sometimes band together during the day to forage on arid land. The largest gelada troop observed by J. H. Crook had 400 members; the smallest consisted of only 30 animals.

During the day geladas and hamadryas tend to

scatter into small foraging units. Food is hard to find in their territory, and the relative absence of predators makes it safer for them to wander. However, where there is also a lack of trees and a scarcity of good high sleeping rocks, the smaller units usually come back together into a troop at nightfall. Hamadryas and gelada units sometimes spend one night with one troop at one sleeping place and the next night with another troop at a different one, provided several suitable sites are available. Their troops are less exclusive than savanna troops in this respect, and they appear to exchange members more readily.

We cannot be sure as yet of the average size of drill and mandrill troops, for the forest dwellers are more difficult to study in the seclusion of their jungle. Groups of up to fifty of each species have been observed. Their social life seems to be more loosely organized than that of the savanna baboons, probably because of the easier life in the rain forest. The same seems to be true of the forest-dwelling anubis of Uganda.

When a savanna baboon troop moves from place to place, its members arrange themselves in a marching order. The pattern is more or less the same in all troops. To the uninitiated observer the troop may seem to be only a haphazard mob, but careful study reveals that the largest, most dominant males keep to the center of the group. From there, they can keep an eye on all the other members. The mothers with infants and the youngsters tend to cluster around the dominant males for protection. The subdominant males and females without infants tend to move along on the outskirts of the troop, with a few of the more aggressive subdominant males moving ahead as an advance guard and a few others bringing up the rear. At rest, the troop arranges itself in roughly the same order. But when a troop is threatened, the dominant males immediately leave the center and go toward the danger, wherever it may be. There they cover the troop while it retreats or they attack the danger directly. It is generally true of all baboons that the males stand to the last against any threat, but it is also true that when they run, they run the fastest.

The smaller baboon social units are called variously, depending on the researcher, the family, grooming cluster, a harem, or one-male unit. The small unit usually consists of a single male, his females and their young, with perhaps one or two bachelor males tagging along. There are also all female and young grooming clusters. Among savanna baboons, grooming clusters rarely separate from the troop and never for more than a few minutes.

The smaller hamadryas units are more venturesome. The hamadryas troop tends to break up during the day, with smaller groups scattering to search for food. Kummer breaks these daytime groups into two classifications: bands and one-male units. A band is composed of several one-male units, and can include from thirty to ninety animals. A one-male unit is composed of one male with from one to nine females, and young. The smallest isolated party observed by Kummer was a single male with six females.

There are also one-male units among the gelada, as well as all-male groups made up of younger males not yet ready to mate and older males. Occasionally a group of females is accompanied by one subadult male.

Drills and mandrills also often forage in family clusters rather than in large groups, as do the forest-dwelling anubis.

All over Africa and Ethiopia baboon troops, bands and family units may be observed going about their business in an orderly and disciplined manner, foraging diligently through the days, marching back to their sleeping places at night. On a normal day, the average savanna troop travels many miles in a circuitous route which usually returns them to the same sleeping place at night. Its range is from three to six square miles in size. There is an estimated population density of about ten baboons to the square mile.

But population varies greatly, depending on the availability of food and protective sleeping places. In the drier lands of the hamadryas, Kummer found only 1.8 baboons per square kilometer (about five-eighths of a mile square). Also, according to Kummer, hamadryas harems or bands do not forage in a circular route, like the savanna baboons, but simply work their way straight out from their sleeping place, then return on a parallel route before nightfall.

The geladas appear to live the most arduous life of all. As we have mentioned, they are dominated by their neighbors, the hamadryas, and usually give way when their territory is invaded. As a consequence, they inhabit the roughest uplands, where their ranges are linear, running along the craglines of gorges and escarpments. At night when sleeping and during the day while foraging, the females and juveniles tend to keep close to the edges of these cliffs, prepared to retreat down the rocks from attack by dogs or men. The males are more likely to stray farther "inland" from the cliff edge, usually keeping themselves between the others and any possible danger. Geladas do not always return to the same sleeping site, but often just keep going for several days, moving along the rocky ridges in their unending search for food, traveling up to four miles a day.

In contrast to the geladas, the forest-dwelling anubis live a relatively easy life in their Uganda jungles. Food is in such abundance that T. E. Rowell found twenty-eight baboons to the square mile and reported that a typical foraging group of anubis had to travel only one to one and a half miles a day in search of food. They, of course, found sleeping trees at hand wherever they chose to halt.

Many animals spend much time and energy marking out and defending the area in which they live. This does not appear to be true of the savanna baboons. The ranges of troops often overlap and they frequently come into contact while feeding, but there is seldom trouble between them, according to Irven DeVore. Two or more troops have been seen drinking side by side at a water hole, although one troop usually waits until the other has finished. It is rumored that in past years, during times of drought, savanna baboons have gathered together into huge troops numbering in the thousands and have migrated together to more verdant territory; otherwise there is limited information about nonhuman primate migrations. On the other hand, there are stories of territorial conflict between the hamadryas and geladas, and we know that the gelada tend to give way before the hamadryas. Also, some hamadryas troops peaceably share sleeping places, while others do not. In general, there does not seem to be much territorial rivalry between baboon species or troops, but the matter is far from settled.

Most monkeys and apes live in the tropical regions. But the baboon, like man, has widened his horizons, often leaving the comparative security of the jungle and venturing out onto the plains and savannas, climbing mountains and learning to swim across lakes and rivers. As we already know, baboons are found in a wide variety of habitats, from coastal swamps and beaches up to mountain snow lines, from the densest jungles to open farmlands. Many baboons still inhabit heavily forested regions, but probably more baboons are found in dry and fairly open country than in any other kind of habitat. Certainly baboons inhabit exposed and barren climates where no other primate except man could survive. Certainly virtually all baboons spend most of their days on the ground. Even the drills and mandrills, which live in the canopy forests, spend most of their time foraging on the forest floor, climbing into the trees only when threatened, occasionally to feed and at night to sleep.

The Kipwezi region in south central Kenya is typical savanna baboon country. The terrain is uneven, with low hills and dry gullies and a few upthrusting heaps of rock. The countryside is dotted with low thorn bushes and mimosa and here and there a cluster of baobab trees. The temperatures are extreme, passing 100 degrees Fahrenheit during an August day, dropping to 44 degrees at night. During the short rainy seasons the streams flood and a growth of rich green vines covers the bushes. During the longer dry seasons, the stream beds dry up and the brush turns brown. During droughts, which may last for as long as two years, there is virtually no water at all, and the countryside begins to fail those who depend on it for food.

Like men, baboons are omnivorous. That is, they are neither strictly herbivores (plant-eaters) nor are they strictly carnivores (meat-eaters). Unlike men, however, baboons do not eat much flesh. Mature males will occasionally kill and eat young birds, rabbits, vervet monkeys and even baby gazelles, but the practice is not frequent and is restricted to certain troops. Meat-eating seems to be learned behavior for baboons, that is, it is not instinctive, but is learned by accident or passed on from one baboon to another. The killing and eating of scorpions varies from troop to troop and seems to be learned behavior, too. Most baboons relish birds' eggs, while some eat crocodile and lizard eggs. Baboons are also fond of honey and the larvae of wasps. Coastal baboons vary their diet with shellfish, including mussels, limpets and crabs.

Nonhuman primates come from insectivore ancestors. Baboons eat many kinds of insects. Drills and mandrills roam the forest floor, overturning rocks and logs and plucking up termites, grubs, worms and grasshoppers.

But the bulk of the baboon diet (around 90 per cent) is vegetable, including berries, grains, the fruit of the prickly pear, and all kinds of flowers and grasses. East African savanna baboons are known to feed from two hundred different plants. Baboons, male and female, young and old, spend most of their day foraging along the ground, plucking seeds and juicy stems from

clumps of brush and lifting rocks and digging with
their hands in search of roots. During dry times, baboons have been known to dig holes two feet deep in
search of moisture-containing roots and bulbs. The
hamadryas locate and dig for subterranean water.

Vegetable matter is not as nutritious as meat. The
herbivore must spend more of its time searching for
and actually chewing and grinding his food than does
the carnivore. Thanks to the development of hunting,
early man was able to augment his diet with protein-
rich meat. But the baboon, which is still primarily a
vegetarian, must spend 80 per cent of its day foraging
for food during the best of times. During times of
drought virtually every moment must be spent grub-
bing and digging simply to stay alive.

In order to range as far as they do in search of
their varied diet, savanna baboons must spend most of
their waking hours on the ground, where they are constantly annoyed by such predators as jackals and
hyenas, lions and cheetahs, and the leopard. The continual necessity to guard against attack by such predators is one of the influences shaping baboon behavior.

This is true in reverse for the hamadryas. The
relative lack of danger from predators in the hamadryas'
desert ranges may account for the fact that the hamadryas troop does not always stay together during the
day and can break up into small bands and one-male
groups. The same may be said for the gelada, which is

also relatively free of the predator threat (except for man). On the other hand, the average hamadryas band still consists of around forty animals, and any gelada group is always ready to scamper back to its cliff edge at the slightest alarm. Much of the male baboon's aggressive alertness can be traced to his desire to keep other males away from his females, as we shall see. Nonetheless, all baboons are constantly on the alert against predation, some to a lesser degree than others. The savanna troops sometimes depend on other animals and birds to help alert them to impending danger.

Throughout much of their range, particularly in the densely populated game reserves, savanna baboons can be seen associating on the ground with other animals such as the gazelle, wildebeest (gnu), hartebeest, zebra, wart hog and giraffe. Less frequently, baboons are seen foraging not far from ostrich, buffalo, rhinoceros and elephant. When elephants move through the troop, the baboons calmly move aside and go on feeding. Buffalo and rhino rarely attack baboons. Long-horned kudu have been seen briefly chasing baboons, but more in a spirit of play than anger.

Some savanna baboons and certain gazelles seem actually to seek out one another and feed together for mutual protection. They recognize one another's warning barks and are almost impossible to take by surprise when foraging together. If the baboons, with their keen eyesight, do not spot a marauding lion or leopard, the gazelles, with their keen hearing and sense of smell, usually do. On most occasions, at the sound of the gazelles' shrill danger bark or the baboons' sharp double bark of warning, the hoofed animals speed away and the baboons scramble up the nearest tree or scale the nearest *krans*—the Afrikaans name for a rock cliff. But sometimes both baboons and gazelles stand their ground. Anthropologists Sherwood Washburn and Irven DeVore once watched while three cheetahs stalked a mixed group of baboon and impala. The impala did not flee, although they are a favorite prey of the cheetah. Before the long-legged cats could close in, a huge male baboon stepped forward threateningly and the cheetahs immediately turned and moved away, leaving the baboons and their hoofed associates to go on eating grass together. It appears that the impala had learned to depend on the male baboons for protection, just as the female and young baboons did.

The troop's primary defense against predators is the size, strength and fighting nature of the mature males. Hyenas and jackals are very wary of male baboons and seldom attack a troop directly for fear of them. Instead, they attack strays: youngsters that have wandered away from the troop or injured stragglers. Cheetahs also prey mostly on the young and the infirm. The giant python and the leopard are most active at night, usually creeping up on the troop's sleeping place, grabbing a victim and dragging it off under cover of darkness.

According to Eugène Marais, who studied baboons for three years in South Africa, the leopard kills its victim swiftly, sinking its fangs into the baboon's lower back and disemboweling it with its claws. However, the leopard can seldom kill quickly enough to stifle the baboon's cry, which immediately alerts the rest of the troop. If the attack takes place at night, the leopard feels free to feed. But if it is in daylight, the troop's males come running and the leopard usually retreats hastily, to wait for nightfall before returning to claim the carcass of its victim.

The carnivores hesitate to confront even one mature male baboon directly, and will flee before threats from two or three full-grown males. Only the lion is without fear of the fiercely protective male baboon.

The male baboon often goes through an elaborate series of threats before attacking. But he is also capable of charging without warning and with considerable speed. It depends on the situation. Like all primates, he will not engage in closed combat if this can be avoided by bluffing. A bleak stare is often enough to bring a troublesome member of the troop into line or to drive away a lingering jackal. Sometimes the stare is accompanied by a quick jerking of the head down and then up, a flattening of the ears against the head, and a pronounced raising of the eyebrows once or twice, while the pale eyelids blink rapidly.

Under stress or excitement the male may grind his teeth or "yawn," opening his mouth to display his sharp canine teeth. Rocking his body forward and backward and slapping or scraping at the ground with his hands can be evidence of uncertainty, but it can also be prelude to an attack. In a similar situation, the male may snatch at tree branches or push at stones, as if in a rage, and he sometimes throws sticks or stones. Possibly a rudimentary use of weapons.

Pushed to the point of actual fighting, the male baboon has a particularly effective method of attack. The final prelude usually involves erecting the ruff of hair around his face and beginning a low grunting. The grunting rises to a crescendo of two-phase, or double, grunts, and the baboon charges forward, grasps his prey with both hands, sinks in his long canines, and pushes away with his hands, tearing out a hunk of flesh in the process.

In defense of his females and young, the male baboon has terrific courage and will fight vigorously. Eugène Marais once watched while a large male leopard stalked a troop of chacma baboons. The big cat was making its way along a narrow rock ledge toward a cave when two male chacmas appeared suddenly on the rocks twelve feet above. As the leopard passed below them, the two baboons leaped onto the leopard. One grasped the cat from behind to immobilize the murderous hindquarters, while the other worked its long eye-teeth into the leopard's throat. Within a few minutes it was over. One of the baboons lay dying, but the leopard was already dead and the troop was safe for the moment.

The average female baboon is not nearly so aggressive as the average male and is less than half his size. Her canine teeth are proportionately even smaller. Such difference between male and female animals is called sexual dimorphism. One function of sexual dimorphism in baboons is that the male, being larger and more aggressive, can better protect the females and young of the troop from predators. Such extreme sexual dimorphism is not prevalent among the tree-dwelling monkeys. Gibbons spend most of their time in the comparative luxury and safety of the trees, and the male and female gibbon are almost identical in size and may be relatively less aggressive than baboons.

Additional information about the extreme difference in size between male and female baboons is to be found in the theory of biomass, which assumes that the availability of food influences animal populations. It has been proved that when the amount of food available in a given territory is reduced by drought or other cause, the number and sometimes the size of the animals in the territory decreases. When the amount of food available increases, the number of animals increases. It appears that animals, baboons included, adjust in population and size according to the available food supply. Female baboons, being smaller, consume less food than the males. In addition, the females mature earlier than males. It would seem that it is advantageous for females to be smaller because the reproductive potential of the baboon group, as measured by the combined body weights of all individuals (biomass), is twice what it would be if males and females were of equal size. The assumption, arrived at by mathematical calculation, is that a number of small females together with a few large mature males form an economic reproductive arrangement or system. In such a group (which also includes immature males) more infant baboons are produced for each given unit of food consumed and the group is better able to perpetuate itself.

But the question persists: Why need the mature males be larger than the females? If they were the same size or even smaller, the group would consume even less food. The answer seems to lie in a combination of the two views. The females are smaller and mature earlier so as to consume less food and produce more offspring. The males are larger so as to better protect the females and offspring.

It also seems to be true that the males are larger as a result of competition between them for possession of the females. Such competition can be intense and has a further, more directly social purpose. The physical strength and fighting nature of the male baboon are important not only in defending the troop against predators but also in maintaining order and discipline within the troop.

It is easy to distinguish the dominant males or "overlords" from the lesser members of the baboon troop. They are often the largest, strongest and most active. Among the savanna baboons, there is usually a central hierarchy, or "supreme council," of three or four overlords at the head of each troop. In the larger troops there may be as many as ten overlords. Beneath this central hierarchy there are the smaller harems or family groups, usually consisting of one male in charge of a number of females, infants and young bachelor males.

Among the hamadryas and gelada there does not appear to be a central troop hierarchy, perhaps because among these species the troop itself is less stable and less important. Kummer considers the one-male unit to be the basic social group among the hamadryas: one male in charge of several females, infants and young bachelor males. Among the gelada, as among most other baboons, there is also a separate group composed mostly of males; the young males not yet able to acquire females, and the old males who have lost their harems. Drills and mandrills also band together and often forage in small family groups, as we have noted.

Whether he governs alone as the head of a harem or as a member of a central hierarchy, the overlord rules firmly. He often occupies the best feeding locations and has access to each female ready for mating. He, either alone or in conjunction with his fellow overlords, determines when and where the troop will move, in search of food, in flight or in attack. Those below him in the troop hierarchy usually defer to him. Should one of them disobey, he usually has only to fix the culprit with a stare or "yawn" and the troublemaker will quickly retreat. Or he may employ threat gestures or a swift drive to achieve the same effect.

A frightened baboon behaves somewhat like a frightened human. First it shrinks back, its eyes starting and its ears flattened back against its head. If the threat persists, the baboon's lips retract from its clenched teeth in a fear grimace, or "frightened grin." The fear grimace is rarely seen in adult males, but females and juveniles grimace readily when threatened by a dominant male. As fear increases, the mouth opens and the baboon may release a nervous stuttering quack, sometimes called a "yakking" sound.

If a female is actually chased and threatened by a dominant male, she runs away screeching. The baboon's scream, whether in pain or fear, is much like that of a human. The female may attempt to placate her attacker by stopping suddenly and "presenting."

Presenting is submissive behavior used as a social mechanism for keeping the peace and expressing the order of ranks and status. The cornered female or juvenile might turn and place her head on the ground, pointing her buttocks toward the male and thus making herself completely vulnerable. Often he then turns away, as if satisfied to have proved himself the stronger.

Presenting it not always so extreme; like the salutes and bows of men, it can be very subtle; a mere dipping of the backside in the direction of the aggressor is often sufficient to divert attack. Although presenting is a part of baboon sexual behavior, as we shall see, it is not strictly sexual. Broadly taken, it is a social signal. One female approaching a mother with infant may present before attempting to touch the infant. A dominant male may even present to another dominant male when approaching the other's space on the sleeping rock.

In the case of the male attempting to establish his dominance over a female: if presenting fails to quiet the male, the female crouches, uttering a long-drawn, high-pitched "churring" version of the screech. The male then grasps the offender, whether female or juvenile, and holds it down long enough to deliver a bite on the back of the neck. The bite is not painless, but it seldom does any real damage.

Most of the time the male does not have to go beyond one of the initial threat stages. He is forced actually to administer punishment no more than once or twice a day, probably less frequently than that. The process of threat-punishment is drawn out and complicated for a reason: to allow as much chance as possible for compromise before actual violence occurs. Like dominance behavior itself, its real purpose is to maintain ordered statuses within the troop by allowing for release of inevitable tensions and by defining each individual's role.

There are other hierarchies of relationships within the troop. There are friendship groups and pecking orders among the bachelor males, among the juveniles and among the females. All these hierarchies and interactional possibilities become particularly apparent through the social ritual known as grooming.

One baboon grooms another by painstakingly picking through its hair, parting the hair with its fingers and picking out dirt, parasites and bits of skin scales with its fingers or teeth. This is the habit which prompted the medieval writer Bartholomew to charge that the baboon was unclean. Actually, thanks to this kind of mutual grooming, the baboon is one of the cleanest animals inhabiting the East African savanna. Although lions are cleanly animals, the backs of their necks, where they cannot reach, are usually covered with ticks. The baboons' hair, on the other hand, is totally free of ticks and other ecto, or skin, parasites.

Within the baboon troop, grooming is also a means of improving social harmony and keeping the peace. To be groomed is apparently an enjoyable experience, like having your hair combed, getting a scalp massage or being caressed affectionately. The groomed baboon lolls on its back or side with its eyes half closed, while its partner works busily away. Obviously, grooming would be an excellent way for one baboon to make up to another, and that seems to be how it is used by juveniles seeking to impress mature males, by females seeking to placate their overlords, and by dominant males in a mating mood to their consorts or sexual partners.

The average baboon spends several hours a day grooming and being groomed. The most active grooming period occurs in the morning, as the troop is preparing to leave the sleeping place. Most grooming is done between animals within what ethologists call the grooming cluster, which usually consists of those animals which gather around any given dominant male, including his current females and their infant offspring. Grooming can also take place outside this one-male unit, as among groups of young subadults and elderly males. But most often, there is a male at the center of the grooming cluster.

Baboons do not "mate for life." The male, particularly the male hamadryas, hangs onto his females zealously. However, he is into his prime by the time he can begin to gather his harem, and the females he takes are young, so that when he has passed his prime, they are often still able to breed. They begin to wander, and he increasingly allows them to stray, and eventually they join some other one-male unit while their former overlord joins the oldsters and subadult males out on the edge of the troop. When a young mother transfers to another harem her new overlord treats her offspring as his own, grooming them and being groomed in return.

Most grooming is done by females and infants, among themselves and for the dominant males. The overlord might groom a female for thirty seconds or so, but then he rolls over languidly and lets her work on him for ten minutes or more.

Grooming is an expression of intense interest in the partner. If a baboon feels that its relationship with another is threatened, it will groom that other. Just as in human society it is often possible to tell who is the most powerful or important by who is the most polite to whom, so it is possible to trace the various pecking orders within a baboon troop by watching to see who grooms whom. The overlord's favorite consort grooms him. The less-favored females groom him and her. The juveniles groom each other, their mothers and the overlord. They all groom and pet the infants, for the babies are immensely attractive to the entire troop. The overlord stays aloof from much of the grooming activity, except when one of his females is in season for breeding, or estrus.

Some experts have claimed that sex is the key to baboon sociability, that it is sex more than anything else that binds the troop together. But this seems unlikely, since primary sexual behavior occupies so little of the average baboon's time in terms of months or years.

The female baboon is in estrus, that is, she seeks copulation with a male, for approximately one week out of every month, if she is neither pregnant nor breast-feeding an infant. As estrus begins, the female's buttocks begin to swell and redden. Within three or four days she is ready to copulate. She approaches the dominant male (or males) first, offering to groom him and eventually presenting, that is, turning and lowering her head so that her backside points toward him. In the beginning, the overlord usually seems to ignore her, although he will often, especially if he is a hamadryas, chase away any of the younger males which show interest in her, and he might punish her with a neck bite if she shows interest in them. Nonetheless, during the first few days she often does mate with one or more of the young bachelor males.

During estrus, her status within the troop hierarchy changes considerably. The males all favor her, and although the other females show signs of jealousy, they have no choice but to respect her temporary rise in position. She may even go so far as to take food away from another female and will be defended in her action by her male consort.

Eventually they form a consort pair and during estrus, the time when she is ovulating and capable of conceiving, the dominant male may drive away the younger males and begin to return the female's advances, grooming her and courting her with grunts and lip-smacking signals. He may even share his food with her, an action not observed in any other situation. They usually move to the edge of the troop to be more or less alone. If the troop's dominance order is not well established, they may be followed by one or more other males and there may be a fight, but usually there is not.

After copulation the male may groom the female, but not so diligently as before. They may stay together for as little as an hour or for as long as several days. As her swelling begins to fade, she returns to her friendship group and the overlord resumes his duties as a troop leader.

Among baboons, as among all mammals, sexual selection is a means of keeping the species strong and making it more adaptable. The strongest, most dominant and most intelligent males tend to survive and breed for many years. Because they attract the females and are able to keep other males away much of the time, they also breed more frequently and usually when the females are most receptive and most likely to conceive. In this way the qualities necessary to survival are passed along from generation to generation.

But social cohesion is also an important mechanism for improving the species' chances for survival, and sex is only one of several forces that act to bind the troop together and keep it organized. In baboon troops, especially small ones, many months may pass without any overt sex occurring; yet no animals leave the troop and its social relationships continue. There is evidence that savanna baboons have breeding seasons. So far there is no evidence of special seasons for breeding among the gelada and forest-dwelling anubis, but such seasons do occur among the hamadryas. Where there are breeding seasons, very little sexual activity takes place for six months out of every year, and yet the troop does not disband. For most of her life, the female baboon is not sexually receptive. She is either a juvenile, is pregnant or is breast-feeding a youngster. Estrus is an important but infrequent event in her life. Yet she does not leave the troop or her harem, not even for a few minutes.

Among the hamadryas and gelada, and probably among the drills and mandrills, the primary social unit is the smaller one-male group, usually consisting of only one overlord, his females, and the infants and juveniles. Such groups may travel during the day with other one-male groups, forming a band, and usually rest with other bands at night. The male hamadryas is extremely jealous of his females and forces them to march directly on his heels wherever he goes. Should they lag behind or stray, he punishes them with a neck bite. Usually he will immediately attack any other male that comes near them. Occasionally an adult male follower is tolerated to such a degree that he might be considered a subordinate leader, but he has no access to females. Apparently the hamadryas does not keep his females exclusively for sexual purposes; long periods pass when none of them are receptive, and frequently a unit is begun when an adult male adopts an immature female whom he cares for and "mothers." In the hama-dryas colony in the Zurich zoo two females stayed with an elderly male for several years after he had become toothless and unable to fight, as well as unable to breed.

It is true that mounting and presenting are common sights among baboons, but these actions are often social ritual rather than sexual actions.

Even when she is not in estrus, the female baboon will turn and present her rump as a signal to the harem overlord. A young male will frequently avert a direct attack from a dominant male by turning and present-ing. Sometimes the dominant male will mount the sub-dominant male, without actual copulation taking place. Usually, however, presenting is enough. Ritual pre-senting and mounting are means of lessening tension within the troop and avoiding physical violence. As with grooming, the careful observer can usually trace the dominance hierarchy within the troop by watching to see who presents to whom.

It is easy to think of the overlord of a harem as an absolute dictator and of the baboon social system as a kind of jungle fascism based purely on physical domi-nance. But it is not that simple.

The overlord has obligations as well as privileges.

There is continual bickering and squabbling in the baboon troop. As principal regulator of order, the overlord often breaks up such petty fights. Usually he is able to restore calm with a steady stare or with a "yawn" threat or other threat gesture. Sometimes, particularly with the young males, he must attack, and on occasion he may be wounded in the course of restoring order. Attacks reinforce and make significant the baboon's signaling system.

Also, when the troop is threatened or attacked, the overlord must lead the defense or counterattack. DeVore and Washburn several times observed predators approaching baboon troops, and almost every time several dominant males were the first to interpose themselves between the predator and the rest of the troop. On one occasion, the scientists placed a stuffed leopard in the path of the moving troop. The first baboon to spot the dummy gave the warning bark, and the dominant males immediately rushed forward and, without hesitation, tore the carcass to pieces.

Another of Eugène Marais' observations concerns a troop that was in the habit of raiding the fields of a South African farm. Its leader always appeared in the fields first and alone. Fired at, he would disappear. But once he has satisfied himself that there was no danger, he would call the rest of the troop out of the trees to join him. Each time the troop came to loot the field, the overlord first risked his life to make sure that the others would be able to feed in safety. Usually this is done by more than one animal.

Baboon watchers have long been puzzled by the fact that the average baboon troop has more mature females than males, despite the fact that the birth ratio of females to males is about equal. There are always some peripheral males living apart from the troop, but they are few. One theory is that many more males than females die violently, defending the troop from predators, among them, increasingly, man.

J. H. Crook found that in those areas where the gelada is free of man's predations, the adult sex ratio was closer to the birth sex ratio; that is, there are as many females as males.

T. E. Rowell also found an equal number of adult males and females among those anubis that live a generally easier life in the forest. But in areas where man hunts the gelada, there are fewer males to lead the bands, and Crook occasionally observed a unit of females accompanied by an immature male. As we know, the males range farther from the safety of the cliffs and are the last to run when danger appears. They are consequently the first to be shot.

On the other hand, there may be additional, as yet unknown reasons for the unbalanced sex ratio among certain species. It is possible that a more arduous life in general is harder on the males, subjecting them to more strain and making them more susceptible to disease. This is another question that we cannot yet answer with assurance.

Although the overlord's power is great, it is not absolute. He is not a dictator but a kind of feudal king, able to rule only with the help of other powerful lords (especially among the savanna baboons). The younger males are continually challenging his authority and testing his strength, usually by attempting to take food or a female away from him. If he heads one of the larger savanna troops, it can be particularly difficult for the dominant male alone to quell such a rebellion of young males. He must depend on the help of other mature males associated with him in the central or ruling hierarchy.

In a troop of macaques studied in Japan, the Number 1, or A-male, Jupiter, often depended for help on the Number 3 male, Pan. On one occasion, the Number 5 male, grabbed a tangerine that Jupiter wanted. Jupiter gave chase, joined immediately by Pan, and the two ran him down and took the tangerine away.

However, where there is no competition for food, there seems to be less struggle for power. Among the forest-dwelling anubis, in their safe and abundant jungles, males and females feed together in relative peace, with few or no hierarchies and a very loose social structure. As always, the ecological situation has a strong influence on social organization.

But wherever there is competition for food or sleeping places, hierarchies tend to form. And hierarchies, depending as they do on cooperation between individuals, can collapse.

When an overlord loses his supporters for one reason or another, he often loses his position of supremacy. In a troop of savanna baboons in Africa described by K. R. L. Hall and Irven DeVore, the central hierarchy consisted of the A-male, Curly, and his friend and second in command, Humbert. Whenever the C-male, Gam, threatened Curly's leadership, Humbert came to Curly's aid and helped put Gam in his place. Then one day Humbert disappeared, presumably shot

Top right: A savanna baboon troop on the march—adult males are at the front on both the left and right sides. Right: Hamadryas sleeping society begins the day's march, with one-male units falling into line.

The adult male full threat shows sharp canines as well as the eyelid threat.

In general, presenting signifies peaceful intentions and acknowledges rank in the troop: above, a female hamadryas presents to the male leader of her unit; below, female hamadryas presents to other females.

Grooming is an important social ritual and serves to keep the baboon free of skin parasites.

or taken by a leopard, leaving Curly alone at the top. During the power struggle that followed, Gam teamed up with an outsider, Lone. Together they defeated the former overlord Curly, and Gam became the overlord, with Lone as his second in command.

It seems that physical strength is not the only quality valuable to the baboon overlord. Like any politician, he must have the ability to get along with others, to enlist and exploit their loyalty. That requires superior intelligence and experience as well as physical strength. In fact, there is evidence that "wisdom" is almost as valuable to a baboon leader as are strong muscles and long canine teeth.

The overlord is not necessarily the largest or strongest baboon in the troop, but he is almost always a seasoned and mature male. He may even be elderly. Zoologist Bruce G. Stringer recalls seeing a number of old patriarchs among the hamadryas of Ethiopia. They were easily spotted because of their snow-white hair, but it was impossible to get near them, for they were protected in the center of the troop. It would seem that they were either greatly feared or greatly valued by the others. Their importance to the troop could not have been a result of physical or sexual dominance, since they were feeble and toothless. It is possible that their value to the troop's survival rested in their long years of experience and learned behavior which had enabled them to survive so long.

5

THE INDIVIDUAL:
Social Behavior of the Baboon

Compared to other animals, the nonhuman primates and men grow up very slowly. This is because they have a lot to learn and need a long childhood in which to learn it. The infant baboon is very dependent on its mother for about a year. The female does not reach social maturity and complete independence until its fourth or fifth year, and in the male maturation takes seven years.

During that time it is learning the lessons basic to its survival, including what to eat and where to find it, who its enemies are and how to avoid them, and how to get along with its fellow baboons. Most of what it has to learn is what is called accumulated knowledge: things that have been learned by baboons of previous generations and have been handed down from baboon to baboon, from mother to infant and from adult males to juveniles and young adults.

Eugène Marais removed an otter and a baboon from their mothers and raised them in isolation. Neither animal was allowed to see its original environment until it was three years old. Then Marais starved both animals and released them. The otter hesitated only a moment, then dove into the water and caught and ate a crab. But the young baboon only wandered aimlessly, confused and unable to feed itself. At one point, it chose a deadly poisonous fruit that no wild baboon raised by its mother would have touched. Marais had to show it how to turn over stones and grub for roots and insects. Eventually the baboon adjusted to the wild environment, but only with the help of Marais, acting as its mother.

The first year with the mother is vital to the young baboon's survival, but the learning process does not stop there. In fact, for the baboon as for all the higher primates, learning is the means of acquiring a way of life, from birth to death.

For baboons, the gestation period, or time from fertilization to birth, can vary in duration from 140 to 210 days. There is a report of a female mandrill being pregnant for 245 days, but the average baboon pregnancy lasts 171 days, or about six months. Outward signs of pregnancy include extension of the abdomen and increase in the size of the mammary glands, or breasts. The prospective mother remains active and forages with the troop right up to the hour of labor or parturition.

Female baboons give birth about every sixteen months and usually have only one infant at a time. Twin births are as rare with monkeys and apes as they are with humans. Apparently the higher primates have developed a tendency to single birth as an adaptation to a tree-dwelling existence. It is difficult enough for a mother monkey to leap from limb to limb with an infant clinging to her belly; it would be doubly difficult with twins, impossible with triplets.

T. E. Rowell has witnessed a number of births among the forest-dwelling anubis. Hans Kummer witnessed a birth while observing a hamadryas sleeping rock. The female separated herself from the troop and moved about two yards away, then squatted with her back to the troop and gave birth. Probably the most closely observed baboon birth to date was recorded in detail in a laboratory. The whole delivery took seven hours and twenty-three minutes. When the infant's head appeared, the mother supported it with her hands and pulled the body gently forth. She then licked her infant clean and ate the placenta. Twenty-three minutes after its head first appeared, the infant was at its mother's breast. It should be noted that this was only one birth, and not enough to establish for certain the normal timing of a baboon birth, let alone normal birth behavior in the wild state.]

The newborn baby baboon looks like a worried little old man with unusually large ears. The face, ears and belly are naked and usually light pink, and the rest of the body is covered by a sparse coat of black hair. At birth, the infant weighs from two to three pounds. Its central nervous system is as well developed as that of a six-month-old human infant, and it is able to support its weight with only the grip of its tiny hands and feet.

The clinging behavior and other adaptation to arboreal life are common to all primate infants. The mother must have her hands free for climbing, and so the infant must be able to support its weight by gripping the mother's fur. Even newborn human infants can support their own weight briefly with their fingers by means of the grasping reflex. Shortly after its birth the mother places the infant against her abdomen, where it clings tightly. When she can, she supports its head with a free hand, but much of the time the infant has to hang on by itself, while the mother goes about her daily business.

The female is active again within an hour after she gives birth.

Baboon mothers are devoted to their young and fiercely protective of them. One observer reports seeing a mother baboon trapped by dogs at the foot of a *krans*. Without the weight of her baby she might have climbed the cliff and escaped, but she refused to abandon her youngster. Instead, she handed the infant to another female on the rocks above, then turned to face the dogs and was killed.

Among baboons there are social advantages in being a mother. Possession of an infant considerably improves the new mother's status within the troop; for all baboons, male and female, are attracted by the very young.

Within a day or two after the birth, other members of the troop begin approaching the mother and attempting to touch and hold the infant. To assure her they mean no harm, they smack their lips, groom her and sometimes present to her by backing toward her with lowered heads and raised rumps. For a week or so she may forbid others to touch her infant, but eventually she allows mature and juvenile females to briefly touch or even hold her youngster. But at the least protest from the infant or the slightest sign of danger from elsewhere, she snatches her baby back. The other females show her the utmost respect and never persist in keeping the infant against her wishes, not even if they are normally higher than she in the troop hierarchy. Being a mother makes her special, at least for the first few months of her baby's life.

The dominant males sometimes ignore the new mother, but often they, too, come to pay their respects and to examine the newborn infant. Sometimes the overlord himself stalks over to inspect the new addition to his troop.

Most other tree-dwelling monkey mothers raise their young apart from the males. But because of the constant dangers of terrestrial life, the infant baboon needs the protection of the males as well as of the females. Male baboons are very protective of both mothers and infants. During the first hour or so after birth, the infant may be slow in clinging adequately to the mother's belly fur. The mother often has to hold the infant to her with one hand, is obliged to hobble along on two feet and one hand, and therefore tends to lag behind the rest of the troop. On several occasions, DeVore and Washburn saw a mature male drop behind and walk along with a new mother, stopping when she stopped to rest, rising with her when she was able to move on again. More than once, when a troop was suddenly threatened and a mother was caught too far away from her baby, one of the dominant males snatched up the infant and carried it out of danger. Male Barbary apes are frequently to be seen carrying infants about and caring for them. But ultimately the infant is always returned to the vital warmth of the mother.

The infant baboon is able to walk at between two and four weeks after birth, but it does not often stray from its mother. Direct and continual contact with the mother during the first few months is essential to the development of the infant into an emotionally normal and healthy baboon. Laboratory experiments with rhesus macaques have shown that infants that are prevented from clinging to a mother's furry warmth grow up to be socially and sexually maladjusted. When such deprived females become mothers themselves, they are usually very bad ones, neglecting their infants and frequently pushing them away. With baboons as with human beings, unhappy mothers usually raise unhappy children.

The infant baboon may take its first solid food at the age of one month, although it continues to get most of its nourishment from its mother's milk. Its baby teeth begin to appear within five days after birth. By three weeks it has its eight incisors.

At about five weeks the infant shifts its riding or carrying position from the mother's belly to the small of her back, where it lies face down, clinging tightly. It frequently returns to her belly for reassurance and to nurse.

By the third month, the youngster is beginning to show interest in the world outside itself and its mother. It occasionally reaches out a tiny hand to touch food which the mother is eating, or grasps a leaf and puts it to its own mouth, usually without actually swallowing. With increasing frequency it hops or hobbles away from its mother and has to be pulled back by the tail. It is no longer a newborn infant, it is a young baboon, growing up and eager to learn.

The mother baboon teaches her baby by example. Watching closely, the baby copies its mother, moving as she does, picking the same plants and leaves that she does, observing how she grooms. Around the fortieth day of its life, the baby begins to return the mother's attentions by grooming her in turn.

It also learns by sensing its mother's inner reactions and learning to read the various tactile and auditory signals of her moods: the touch of her hands, the expression of her eyes, the sounds she makes. It senses and learns to share its mother's avoidance of the dark, of snakes and of the various other scents and signs of dangers. It also learns to share its mother's friendlier attitude toward other baboons, her interest in other females, her respect for the dominant males.

By the fourth month the infant frequently ventures away from its mother for brief periods of time, but it scampers obediently back at a signal from her. Its social relationships begin as it crawls near and even over the dominant males. For the most part they tolerate it and might even briefly groom the youngster, grunting rapidly as they do so. In this way, the infant begins to learn the various placating grunts and warning barks of baboon vocal language.

By the fifth month, the baby baboon begins to sit up, jockey-style, on its mother's back, lying face down only when the mother runs or climbs. It may occasionally be seen riding a mature male the same way.

By now it has its canine teeth, is getting its premolars, and is taking solid food regularly. It also begins to use its cheek pouches for storing food. When taking food by hand, it frequently rolls the food on the ground with the flat of its palm or between the palms of its hands, breaking or crushing it before putting it in its mouth. This appears to be a pattern of action that cleans the food. It is especially prominent when the food is grit covered. Mature baboons have learned to wash their food, in the wild and in captivity.

Also by its fifth month, the baby moves as much as twenty yards away from its mother, picking up objects such as sticks and stones and generally exploring and learning about its environment. Its coat of hair has begun to thicken and at the same time to change from black to light brown. Possibly this color change causes the other adults to cease treating the young animal as an infant. They still come to its aid when it is in trouble, but they no longer groom or hold it. It is not without social relationships, however. It is beginning to play with other youngsters of its own age.

All young monkeys and apes play vigorously. It is their way of expending energy, of developing physical strength and skills, of exploring and learning about the world around them and of relationships with their fellows.

The youngsters of the baboon troop are almost continually on the move, running, wrestling, somersaulting, exploring. Marais once watched while a bunch of baboon youngsters whooped and wrestled at the end of a tree branch above a stream, trying to push one another off into the water. Young baboons chase one another through the troop while it is at rest. Sometimes they annoy their elders with their antics and are punished. Marais recalls seeing an old male dunk a troublesome youngster headfirst in a waterhole.

By the ninth or tenth month, the young baboon is ready to begin the process of leaving its mother.

Baboon mothers wean their young at between five to ten months. It is usually in the youngster's tenth month of life that the mother begins to push it away from her and refuse to let it ride on her back. The process is gradual, taking between one and four months. Normally, by its first birthday, the youngster is weaned from nursing its mother. Now when danger threatens, the young baboon tends to flee to the protection of a dominant male and not to the mother. It is relating less and less to its mother and more and more to the troop as a whole, and to its friendship group in particular.

During the second year of its life the young juvenile continues to learn the basic lessons of baboon citizenship by spending most of its day with its peers, youngsters of its own age. They feed together during the day and play together early and late at the sleeping place. They learn by watching the adults and by direct discovery, and they pass on what they have learned to one another. They learn to eat an egg by punching a hole in one end, upending it and sucking it dry. They learn to drag honeycombs through the grass to rid them of stinging insects. They learn to recognize the plants and animals that will do them harm as well as those that are beneficial. Perhaps most important of all, they learn to get along with one another.

A baboon that grows up without social contact with other baboons of its own age will never be able to interact properly in baboon troops. In laboratory experiments by Professor Harry Harlow, a number of rhesus macaques were raised in complete isolation. Others were raised in sight of other monkeys, and still another group was isolated from all other monkeys except their mothers.

Those macaques raised entirely alone grew up to be seriously maladjusted. They made stereotyped movements, or they trembled and shrank away from objects that moved. Those raised within sight of other monkeys but prevented from touching or playing with them grew up unable to establish normal social and sexual relationships. They were not entirely incapacitated, but they were unfriendly and couldn't copulate normally.

Surprisingly, those macaques raised only with their mothers were also unable to establish satisfactory social relationships with other baboons. It seems that the presence of the mother alone is not enough. A young baboon must have the company of others its own age in order to grow up to have normal social relationships and it must engage extensively in varied play.

The young baboon forms relationships in its friendship group that will last all its life. Friends and enemies are made, and the dominance hierarchy begins to form during play. The young male that leads its fellows in play-fighting is likely to grow up to lead them as overlord. The young female who is stronger, more intelligent and more attractive than her friends is likely to grow up to lead the troop's female hierarchy.

It seems that with baboons, as with humans, leadership often runs in the family. According to recent field studies of rhesus macaques, active and dominant juveniles often have active and dominant mothers. The most obvious reason for this is that strong begets strong: physically superior parents are likely to produce physically superior offspring.

But the aristocrat has an additional advantage: confidence. A mother at the bottom of the troop hierarchy lives in continual fear of harassment and attack and is, therefore, nervous and lacking in confidence. She is likely to raise youngsters that are equally nervous and anxiety-ridden. On the other hand, juveniles that grow up around self-assured and confident adults are likely to be confident and self-assured themselves. And in baboon disputes, self-confidence is often a vital factor.

During the young baboon's third year, a good many physical changes take place. Permanent dentition commences, and within the year the young baboon usually has grown its full set of adult teeth. The muscles of the arms, legs and back develop considerably, and the bone structure of the face develops a more elongated profile. The first signs of adult coat and coloring begin to appear. The young savanna male begins to develop cheek ruffs and the shoulder mantle. Touches of gray begin to appear in the coat of the young hamadryas, and the males begin to develop the cape of hair. The young drills and mandrills begin to take on the colorful markings of the adults. The young gelada begins to develop its incredible pushed-up muzzle and heart-shaped chest patch.

The three-year-old baboon weighs between ten and fifteen pounds, with the males already somewhat larger than the females. Both males and females continue to spend most of their time with their peers. But the play gets rougher and the lessons harder.

The mother will continue to favor her own offspring all her life, but she probably has a new infant now and cannot spare much time for her older juveniles. The other adults of the troop are less and less tolerant of the juveniles. The young male finds himself frequently threatened by the adult males. The young female finds that as the adult males begin to show interest in her, the adult females begin to become jealous.

She is rapidly approaching sexual maturity. Occasionally, she prepares for her maternal role by adopting an infant or surrogate juvenile with which she plays for brief periods of time.

Baboons are fascinated by most small creatures. Adults and young alike have been known to play with and keep lizards, puppies, piglets, goats, ducklings and baby monkeys. Charles Darwin was fond of telling of a captive baboon that kept a succession of pets, including a baby kitten. When the kitten persisted in scratching, the baboon examined its paws and bit the tips of the claws off, one by one.

While baboons of all ages and both sexes have been known to adopt pets, most of these volunteer foster parents are young, and usually they are female. Marais tells of a young female that kept a baby rabbit, holding it to her belly as she would a baboon baby and trying to suckle it.

At the same time that the young females are preparing for their maternal roles, the juvenile males are preparing to fill their roles by play-fighting and establishing dominance among themselves. With the onset of full adolescence, a gradual separation of the sexes occurs.

By the end of her fourth year the female baboon has passed through or is beginning puberty. That is, she is in the process of becoming sexually mature. Her sexual cycles have begun, she is almost fully grown, and her behavior is for the most part that of an adult. She may linger with her friendship group for a few more months, but usually between her second and fourth year she leaves the other juveniles and joins the grooming clusters of adult females.

Even though still immature, she may be taken up by one of the dominant males, especially if she is a hamadryas. Adult hamadryas males sometimes adopt immature females, on occasion going so far as to carry them on their backs over difficult terrain. From such an early relationship between a young mature male and an immature female, a new family unit often begins.

During her first sexual cycle, our young female may not actually breed, but by the second or third she is ready to join the males, if she has not already done so. She becomes the consort of one of them, often one of the dominant males. Within six or seven months she is likely to be a mother. From that point on her life will probably be pretty much the same from year to year. She will be in estrus, will breed, will give birth, and will raise one infant about every twelve to sixteen months. She may ascend a few rungs in the female hierarchy as she grows older and wiser. And she may pass on some of her learned wisdom to her later off-spring.

The male baboon takes much longer than the female to reach maturity. Although he is probably ready to mate by the end of his fourth year, he is neither strong enough nor aggressive enough to claim more than passing attention from the mature females.

For the next four years of his life, the young male is forced to spend his days on the periphery of the troop with the other bachelors. If he is a young male gelada, he may join a separate all-male group. By his fifth year he is larger than most full-grown females and is capable of establishing dominance over them. But he is still much smaller than the full adult males. He tends to avoid the overlords, and they, in turn, keep him away from the females. Occasionally he may mate with a female early in her estrous cycle, but when a dominant male threatens him, he usually flees.

Finally, between his eighth and ninth years, the male reaches full maturity.

In his prime, which he reaches between the ages of seven and ten, the male baboon has full skeletal and muscular growth and a full set of permanent teeth, including the formidable canines. His coat is thick and long, with deep ruffs at the cheeks and a thick mantle down the shoulders. If he has not already fought part of the way to his place in the dominance hierarchy, he is ready to begin now. If he is a hamadryas, drill or gelada, he has probably acquired at least one female and will acquire more for his harem, if and when they are available. He will continue in his prime until his thirteenth or fourteenth year, in some cases for several years after that.

The female, who has reached her prime between four and five years of age, will continue to breed and produce infants until her fourteenth year, sometimes later.

By now the mature male or female has mastered the varied and complex vocal and other signals of baboon communication. The baboon has a wide vocal range and is capable of producing an incredible variety of sounds. Probably the first sound the newborn baboon infant makes is the stuttering quack that goes something like *ehck-ehck-ehck* or *kek-kek-kek*. It indicates pain or fear and varies from soft to loud, depending on how uncomfortable the infant is. By the time the baboon has reached maturity, it has mastered dozens of distinct vocal signals. A partial list of baboon vocalizations is included in the appendix, pages 143–146. Each known signal also has dozens of subtle variations, few of which have been analyzed for meaning; but this is a challenging and rapidly growing field of study.

We have discussed the sounds and gestures occurring in threat-attack and fear-escape situations. There are also distinct communication patterns for more friendly occasions.

After a separation, friendly baboons greet one another with placating grunts and lip-smacking, sometimes standing briefly opposite one another on hind legs, then approaching for a half-embrace, hands on one another's shoulders or rump, faces close together and sniffing, sometimes "kissing" with the extended tip of the tongue. Young chacma baboons have been heard to greet one another with an intermittent chattering call. Baboons separated from the troop during the day sometimes utter a loud high-pitched bark when approaching the group again.

Infants at play are capable of a number of pleasure sounds, including a giggle which can rise in volume and excitement until it becomes something very like human laughter.

During fights within the troop or attack against outside predators, adult male baboons are capable of a crescendo of grunts rising into a whopping roar that can be heard as far as the roar of a lion.

A startle reaction occurs when a baboon is unpleasantly surprised, as by the sudden appearance of a snake. The baboon usually rises on its hind legs and jumps back, arms spread, releasing a shrill warning bark.

In confusion or uncertainty a baboon may make a vague circular gesture in front of its face, sometimes also uttering the sharp yakking sound that usually accompanies the fear grimace. Faced with a difficult or uncertain situation, a baboon will often gaze off in another direction, scratch its arms or back, shrug its shoulders or fiddle aimlessly with food. This is called displacement activity and is the animal's attempt to put off facing the difficulty, much as a man under pressure may deliberately light a cigarette or elaborately clear his throat.

Finally, baboons are apparently capable of mourning their dead with a cry which Eugène Marais described as "purely emotional—more or less similar to the inarticulate groaning and sighing by which the deepest anguish of the human heart finds speechless expression."

By the time of their maturity, the average male and female baboon have absorbed most of the accumulated knowledge of their immediate family, their friendship group, their troop, their species. This does not mean, however, that all baboons learn exactly the same things and adopt exactly the same behavior patterns.

The kind and amount of knowledge acquired by individual baboons can vary greatly. One reason for this is that baboon knowledge and behavior vary from species to species and from troop to troop. Living in the rain forest as they do, drills and mandrills have extensive knowledge of jungle roots and fruits, whereas the savanna and other species of baboon are more knowledgeable about the foods found on the dry and rocky grasslands. The hamadryas males are extremely jealous of their females, whereas the savanna males seem to be less so. Obviously, a hamadryas youngster learns a somewhat different attitude toward females than does the savanna youngster. As we have seen, he must learn the ins and outs of a different social organization.

Variations in knowledge and behavior are also found in different troops of the same species. In one hamadryas troop, it may be common practice to "thresh" wild wheat by whacking handfuls of it against the rocks, while in another troop the practice may be unknown. Members of some savanna troops kill and eat other animals, while others do not. Members of some savanna troops are expert at removing the sting from scorpions and eating them, while others flee in terror at the mere sight of a scorpion. The savanna youngster can grow up to loathe meat and scorpions, or he can grow up to relish one or both, all depending on the troop into which he happens to have been born.

There are also variations in knowledge and behavior between individual baboons within the same troop. A mature male has been observed using his tail as a sponge to soak up water from a shallow waterhole, while the rest of his troop bent nearby and sucked at the muddy water with their lips in the usual manner. There is no record as to whether the troop eventually adopted the innovation; but if they did, it would not have been the first time that individual inspiration had been passed on to the rest of a troop.

Variations between individuals can be extreme in primates. When C. R. Carpenter transplanted a colony of rhesus macaques to uninhabited Santiago Island in the Caribbean, they soon divided up into six groups and settled down. Each group kept to its patch of territory and there was relatively little trouble between the troops for a time. Food was regularly provided by a caretaker, and there was plenty for all. Nonetheless, one of the troops began to infringe on the territory of the others, eventually making feeding excursions into the territories of five other troops. Carpenter discovered that the aggressive troop contained a male of supreme dominance. This male was removed, and the aggressive activities of the group were reduced immediately. He was then replaced, and his troop immediately resumed its imperialistic activities and spread its range.

Certainly individual variation is very rarely so extreme, as Professor Carpenter would be the first to point out. We use this case to make our point only because most of us tend to view other animals as more or less all the same and without the individual variation we note among humans. With primates, as with humans, individual variation may produce positive results. During field experiments with wild Japanese macaques, one juvenile female took to washing her sweet potatoes before eating them. Soon her mother was doing the same, then her playfellow, and finally most of the colony had acquired the new habit. The young female had "invented" a new feeding custom. One could say that she had stumbled upon the habit by chance, but it seems more likely that the variation in custom was the result of variation in the individual.

More so than other mammals, the nonhuman primates have this ability to acquire new knowledge and invent new behavior. They are able to take the creative initiative and actually alter ingrained or so-called instinctive behavior.

For many years, students of human and animal behavior have tried to distinguish between instinctive and learned behavior. The animal was supposedly born with its instincts, but was born without certain other knowledge, which had to be taught to it during its lifetime.

Modern ethologists have come to realize that animal behavior is not to be divided up so simply. For example, it might be assumed that baboons would instinctively sniff all strange foods before trying them, but it is not certain that baboon infants test food in this manner before their third or fourth week of life. Also, so-called instinctive behavior can be radically altered. It had always been assumed that sexual behavior was to a great extent instinctive, yet rhesus macaques that have been deprived of natural companionship from birth and reared in isolation grow up unable to perform the basic sex act.

Much of the time we cannot reliably tell the difference between behavior which is prompted by knowledge stored in the genes of the newborn and behavior prompted by knowledge which the young baboon acquires from others or develops through personal experience. Inspiration for most behavior comes from sources that are far too complicated for us to fully understand.

We can describe primate behavior as resulting from a complex process of individual learning within a wide range of genetically and socially determined possibilities. It may seem to some that the infant baboon is given too wide a range of possibilities for its own good. The otter is born with a much narrower range of possibilities for behavior, and Marais' otter was able to feed itself without the help of a mother, whereas the young baboon might have starved or poisoned itself without Marais' help in learning how to find food.

Primate infants are very vulnerable during their first years because of their dependency on the mother and the troop, and their relative lack of instinctive knowledge. On the other hand, because they do their learning within such a wide range of possibilities, they grow up to be far more flexible and creative in their behavior.

Of all the primates, the baboon equals the macaques and is second to the anthropoid apes in its ability to adapt to new situations. When an otter is faced with a drastic alteration in its natural scheme of things or is frustrated in normal endeavor, it is likely either to go right on behaving as before, no matter how disastrous such action might be, or simply to become confused. But the baboon, because it has been a learning creature from birth, is more likely to follow initial confusion with careful study, and eventually change its behavior to meet the new situation.

For as long as there have been lions, baboons have been climbing trees to escape them. One might think that it would have become instinctive for baboons to climb trees to escape danger. However, recently men have been carrying guns, with which they can easily shoot baboons out of the trees. Baboons still climb trees when lions appear; but when men appear, they climb down from the trees and run away. They have even learned to distinguish men with guns from those without.

Eugène Marais reported watching a troop of chacma baboons shaking down the fruit of the baobab tree. Discovering that they were unable to open the tough fruit with their teeth, the chacmas took the large nuts to some nearby rocks and banged them against the stone. When that failed to open the fruit, they picked up stones and pounded the nuts until the inner kernels were finally broken free. This is, of course, a perfect example of the rudimentary use of tools.

Such new or innovative behavior starts first with an individual, then spreads through the troop. However, the ability or willingness to try new approaches seems to be more common to the younger members than to the elder ones.

It was discovered during the field study of wild

Japanese macaques that most feeding innovations were initiated by young adult monkeys. It was a young female that had first washed her potato, and it was the youngsters that first began accepting candy from the scientists. First the youngsters tried it, then the sub-adults, then the adults, until finally, after several months, the whole troop had made the change, with the exception of a few conservative old males that refused to touch the candy.

On the other hand, it was found that when one of the older macaques, such as a dominant male, introduced some new detail of behavior, the rest of the troop was much quicker to accept it. Apparently the mature animals are more trusted. It seems that the conservatism of mature males and females and the old patriarchs serves as a necessary check on the easy enthusiasms of the young.

The baboon is adaptable, that is, it is able to change to meet new conditions. Mere change is not the objective, however. Like all other social mechanisms, adaptability has as its objective the survival of the species.

Without the troop, the individual baboon could not survive under most conditions. The malformed, the sick and the injured fall behind and die of thirst or hunger, succumb to disease or are taken by predators. An injured or sick baboon may receive help for a while. There are reliable reports of dominant males carrying injured or diseased juveniles on their backs. But sooner or later a sick or injured baboon that cannot keep up with the troop must perish.

Young bachelor males sometimes separate voluntarily from the troop, but they usually return as they approach their prime and are ready to assume dominant positions. Occasionally an adult male will leave the troop and live separately but interactively with the group. But the fact remains that the troop is a necessary condition for normal life of the baboon.

On the other hand, without vigorous and creative or nonconformist individuals, the troop is lost. Almost always new and valuable knowledge is first discovered by a single individual, then transmitted to the rest of the interactive population. While baboon society has as its objective the preservation and improvement of the species, it has a complementary purpose: the instruction and improvement of the young and the fostering of individual initiative and excellence. Without the troop, the individual baboon doesn't have a chance, but without vigorous new generations producing outstanding individuals, the troop weakens, and the species is unable to adapt to change and degenerates.

Baboons live on the average for from twenty to twenty-five years. There are many records of baboons living in captivity for over thirty years. Several captive baboons have lived beyond forty, including a white-haired old male hamadryas that has lived in the San

Antonio Zoo for forty-five years and is still able to get around its cage.

There are no baboon death statistics. As we shall see in the next chapter, it is known that baboons are susceptible to heart disease, intestinal parasites, viruses, and a number of other ailments often fatal to men. Certainly most baboons die of disease or infection rather than violently. It is generally agreed among ethologists that most baboons die while trying to keep up with the troop. They are usually left where they have fallen. Africa's various carrion-eaters see to it that the remains are gone within hours.

Left: The baboon infant clings to its mother's abdomen; above: by the fifth month the baby is able to ride jockey-style on its mother's back.

Above: By the fifth month the baby is beginning to play with others its own age—developing its strengths and skills and exploring new social relationships.

The hamadryas one-male unit often begins with an adult male adopting an immature female; right: a male returns to carry one such female over a section of rock that is too difficult for her to cross by herself.

6

HUNTED:
The Baboon and Man

Probably man first hunted the baboon for food. As we know, the man-ape *Australopithecus* used his first weapons to kill baboons, among other animals. He had not learned about fire, so he must have eaten his prey raw. Monkeys are still used for food in some primitive societies, and baboons are cooked and eaten by some natives of Africa and Arabia.

Because they are so common in Africa, baboons are seldom shot for trophy. Occasionally an unusually large male will be shot for mounting or a patriarch will be shot for its white pelt. Baboons are also killed to be used as bait by hunters seeking such larger game as leopard. But trophy hunting is mostly a sport of the privileged and accounts for a very small percentage of baboon deaths.

However, thousands of baboons are hunted and killed by man in Africa every year as vermin.

Baboons have been raiding fields ever since men have been cultivating them. They gather up chicken eggs, strip orchards and are particularly fond of corn, an African staple. A large troop can destroy several acres of corn in a few hours, knocking the stalks down and leaving on the ground what they do not eat or carry away.

For centuries native African farmers have been enduring baboon raids, and a whole baboon folklore has grown up as a result. Some of the tales are quite unlikely, while others are probably true.

One tale would have it that certain large males are in the habit of tying ropes around their middle so that they might carry away more loot by thrusting ears of corn into these makeshift belts, but even the most ardent admirers of baboon ingenuity have to discount it. The story may be a fanciful elaboration of the fact that a determined baboon is capable of carrying five ears of corn—one under each arm, one in each hand, and one in its mouth.

One of the most persistent stories of baboon cleverness holds that baboon raiders guard themselves against surprise attack by posting sentries. Many African farmers and hunters insist that baboon raids are planned and carried out with commando-like precision. They say that scouts are first sent in to select the best field and to check for men with spears or guns. If the scouts report that the coast is clear, the main body then moves into the field. Sentinels are posted at strategic points. Some farmers say the sentries climb lookout trees in pairs, sitting back to back so that they can watch in all directions. If danger appears, the sentinels give the alarm bark. The troop then flees, the males bringing up the rear, the females and juveniles hurrying ahead.

It is generally agreed in Africa that baboons also post guards around their sleeping places at night. Mrs. Delia Akeley, wife of an American zoologist, sat up four nights in Kenya watching a troop of baboons and reported that the baboons stood guard duty in five-hour shifts. The first sentries went on duty at sunset and were replaced punctually at eleven-thirty each night.

Field observers have reported seeing dominant male baboons sitting on high rocks and "scanning" the surrounding countryside, that is, looking about themselves in a full 180-degree arc every minute or so. Other scientists have observed a troop crossing a road used by men. The dominant males watched over the others, seeing to it that they bunched up for the crossing, standing guard as the troop crossed, then bringing up the rear.

Beginning in the first quarter of the last century, European farmers began to settle in Africa in increasingly large numbers, particularly in Kenya and South Africa. As more and more land was taken over, baboons and men came increasingly into conflict. Those baboons closest to the spreading farms soon began to develop new habits and behavior with which to adapt to the new conditions imposed by the invaders. Although they were not normally meat-eaters, baboons learned to kill lambs and open their stomachs to get at the curdled milk inside. The habit apparently first appeared during hard times in the drought-stricken areas of the Cape province, but it soon spread throughout South Africa, and before long, the baboons were eating the flesh of the slaughtered lambs as well as taking the milk. They even learned to skin the lambs expertly and to drain them of blood, as men do. Before long, some South African baboons were killing and devouring full-grown sheep, pigs, ducks, chickens, turkeys and, occasionally, domestic dogs and cats. They tore down fencing, wire enclosures and whole chicken-houses in order to satisfy their new appetite.

Such activities, while limited only to certain troops, soon gave baboons a bad reputation among the farmers of South Africa. In addition, there were the old native horror tales to haunt the European new-comers, among them the legend that baboons habitually stole human infants and raised them as their own.

There are a number of recorded cases of baboons stealing human babies. We have seen how attractive all infant creatures are to baboons and how strong the maternal instinct is in the female baboon. Given a primitive society where human infants are often left unguarded at the edge of fields, it seems likely that a baboon mother that has lost her own infant might be tempted to steal a human baby and raise it as her own. However, in most cases the baby probably was not stolen at all. Most of the "wolf boys" of India and other underdeveloped countries were babies that had been abandoned in the jungle by their parents because of illness or abnormality, or for religious reasons. The same is probably true of most "baboon children."

One of the best documented stories of such a "baboon boy" dates back to 1903. The troopers of the South African Cape Mounted Police were on patrol when they spotted a troop of baboons fleeing a corn-field. Giving chase, they noticed that one of the troop was having trouble keeping up with the rest, then they saw that it was not a baboon but a young native boy. Capturing him, they took him to a mental hospital, where he was named Lucas. He ran on all fours, showed his teeth and barked like a baboon. He would eat nothing but prickly-pear fruit and grubs. After a year, he was released from the hospital and put to work as a fieldhand. Like most such "wild boys," Lucas never learned to talk and so was unable to say whether or not he had been raised by baboons. He died a few years after his capture.

Eugène Marais tells the story of a pet chacma baboon which became very fond of the infant child of its South African owners. One day the baboon broke its chain, scooped up the child and climbed to the top of a tree. The baboon couldn't be shot out of the tree for fear of injuring the child, so a Bushman was sent for. The native "talked" the baboon into coming down from the tree and giving up the child. The baby was unhurt except for a few scratches from tree branches. The baboon was shot.

Such incidents only contributed further to the distaste with which the farmers and stockmen of South Africa and other populated areas came to regard the baboon. They wasted no time in declaring the animal vermin and putting a price on its head. However, it turned out to be much easier to condemn the baboon than to exterminate it. Baboons quickly learned the ways of human hunters.

Around 1850 a traveler wrote of watching while a troop of hamadryas baboons drove Ethiopians from their fields, ignoring stones thrown by the irate farmers. A large posse from the village eventually returned to chase the baboons, "but even then they only retired slowly, seeing that the men had no guns."

Many hunters, native and European alike, are convinced that certain experienced male baboons know the comparative range of a spear, a bow and a gun.

There is no doubt that some baboons can tell a man with a gun from one without. Not only that, but they can tell the difference between a woman and a man, and they will readily drive a woman from the fields. One farmer, hoping to take advantage of the baboons' disdain for women, dressed himself up as a woman and hid his shotgun under his skirt. He managed to entice the troop close enough to shoot one male, but the others fled. The baboons never mistook him for a woman again, no matter how many petticoats he put on.

Attempts to exterminate baboons with poison have not been very effective. Most troops have long ago learned to detect the smell of strychnine in just about any food. The poison has to be put into sealed capsules and well hidden inside the bait; and even then, once a few baboons have died of eating such bait, the remainder often refuse to eat any food that is not fresh. What is more, such precautionary behavior can persist in a troop for years afterward.

The most effective of the early attempts to eliminate baboons were the organized drives employing large numbers of native beaters. The beaters would encircle the troop, often while it slept at night, then close in until the Europeans were close enough to use their guns. Even then, the males often escaped by charging through the line of beaters, and occasionally a bold overlord was able to lead his whole troop through the lines under cover of darkness.

Mounted Boer farmers still make it a custom to ride down baboon troops, firing into their midst; but this practice can be dangerous. On one occasion, near Kimberley, a galloping rider was aiming at a big male when the running baboon grabbed the horse's foreleg and threw both horse and rider. Only the man's shotgun saved him from being torn to pieces by the troop.

Baboons can be fierce in taking advantage and merciless in exploiting. Occasionally a hunter armed with a rifle is charged by large and determined males. Lone natives armed with spears have been stalked, surrounded and attacked by baboon gangs. One reported throwing a spear at a big male, only to have the baboon pick up the spear and throw it back—wrong end first.

Do baboons make rudimentary use of tools? We have mentioned Marais' story about the chacmas using stones to break open the fruit of the baobab tree. There are not many other authenticated stories of baboons using tools in the wild. In fact, Dr. Jane van Lawick-Goodall has observed chimpanzees using straws to pull out termites while baboons stood by without imitating them, although they also relish termites.

This does not mean that all baboons are incapable of using tools. Captive baboons have been taught to use tools in experimental situations. Baboons in zoos occasionally use sticks for leverage in their attempts to pry the bars of their cages loose. Further field study may yet reveal that at least some wild baboons make use of crude tools.

There is no question that baboons throw sticks and stones. The controversy is over whether they take deliberate aim or only fling the objects at random. Those who doubt the baboon's deliberate use of weapons point out that it is common displacement behavior for a nervous baboon to grasp a bush or a stone and shake it and often to tear off branches or bits of stone and fling them. But they claim that there is no evidence that the baboon takes deliberate aim or throws the objects for purposes of hitting anybody. The field researcher K. R. L. Hall reports being showered with stones by a baboon troop moving along a ledge above him, but feels that the stones were probably accidentally dislodged.

There is the testimony of hundreds of Africans, native and European, that baboons do throw sticks and stones. Eugène Marais tells of pet chacmas that threw tin cups full of water at people they disliked, and there are countless authenticated reports of baboons in zoos throwing bits of carrot and feces at the public. The noted zoologist Ivan Sanderson tells of being surrounded in the jungle by a group of angry drills, among them several vigorous males that repeatedly ran forward to fling stones and bits of stick at him. The zoologist was beginning to wonder if he would ever escape when one of the infants ran forward, grimacing fiercely in imitation of its elders, tossed a tiny clod, then scooted back again. The sight was so comical that Sanderson burst out laughing, and at the sound the astonished drills turned and fled.

During the first part of this century many African governments declared the baboon to be a pest and offered a bounty for each one killed. Professional bounty hunters joined the farmers in their campaign to exterminate the baboon. Traps were used with some effect and are still being used successfully by trappers seeking animals for medical and other research use. But the most effective method of killing baboons has turned out to be the use of trained dogs. A fast dog can outrun a baboon in open country, and when the fugitive baboons hide themselves among the rocks of some *kop*, or solitary outcropping of rock, the dogs are often able to smell them out and kill the females and juveniles. However, no dog is a match for a big male baboon. A dominant male will often lure a dog away from the rest of the pack and then turn on him suddenly. Females will sometimes entice the dogs into a narrow gully where the males are waiting. The hunters themselves have to guard against these ambushes. Several men have been pushed off cliffs by baboons. Occasionally a big male will grab a hunter's leg long enough for the other males to overwhelm him, gun and all.

Charles P. Skoda, who hunted baboons professionally for several years in Kenya, recalls an old male troublemaker that he never did manage to get. At the game of hunting and being hunted the old rogue was the equal of any animal, including man, according to Skoda.

Between 1925 and 1927 the South African government paid out over $24,000 in baboon bounties, and yet the baboon problem showed no sign of being solved. In fact, as the population of the cities and towns increased, baboons have caused more trouble in urban areas. In the suburbs of Cape Town, a troop of seventy baboons invaded the home of millionaire yachtsman T. O. M. Sopwith; and when one of the servants attempted to stop them, the baboons pushed the man out the window.

Baboons are still poisoned, ridden down and rounded up, trapped and shot as pests. But the baboon is adaptable and is learning to adjust to its environment, man included. Thanks to an improved diet of corn, wheat, melon and lamb, it actually appears to be thriving in many of those places where it is the most intensively hunted. The baboon is actually increasing its numbers in a few areas of Africa.

But the baboon cannot hold out forever against the growing population and rapid modernization of Africa if its environment is destroyed. As more and more land comes under cultivation, the baboon's nat-

Savanna baboons in Kenya National Park

ural habitat will be proportionately reduced and the troops will increasingly depend on man's fields for their food. As the baboon comes more and more to threaten the survival of the hungry peoples of Africa, governments will be compelled to take effective action against them.

Public opinion already runs strongly against the baboon on his home continent, particularly in Kenya and South Africa. In fact, in 1964 the South African government went so far as to make it against the law for individual citizens to keep baboons as pets, a practice that has a long tradition in Africa, where baboons have not always been trapped only for purposes of extermination.

7

CAPTURED:
The Baboon and Man

Men capture and keep baboons for various purposes, ranging from the purely predatory habit of eating them to the purely sentimental desire to make friends with them. Men have been keeping monkeys and apes as pets since prehistoric times. In certain South American tribes monkeys are raised for eating, and the women of the tribes often breast-feed infant monkeys until they are old enough to take solid food. In the same way, Bushmen women sometimes suckle baby baboons, raising them to be used for magical purposes and as watchdogs.

Until 1964 many South African farm women kept tame baboons to watch over and sometimes wet-nurse their babies. In some ways the female baboon makes an excellent nanny. She never lets the baby out of her sight, will play with it for hours on end and will defend it to the death. The trouble is, the baboon nanny can grow to be very possessive of her charge and may even attempt to keep the mother away from her own child. She may also insist on sleeping in the same crib with the child and may attempt to teach it such baboon arts as killing scorpions and climbing rocks.

Baboons have been trained to serve men in many other ways, beginning at least as far back as ancient Egypt, where animal training was a highly respected activity—probably exclusive to the priesthood. Egyptian sculptures and paintings, which humanize animals, show baboons playing the harp and lute, dancing, riding horses and dogs, harvesting fruit, serving and drinking wine, sweeping floors, turning irrigation treadmills, docking barges and writing with pen and papyrus. The Egyptian Book of the Dead shows three hamadryas baboons pulling in a net full of fish. Of course, many of these representations are fanciful.

Baboons have no ear for music, although a pet baboon owned by zoologist Gerald Durrell was fond of jumping up and down among human dancers and of pummeling a drum. Modern attempts to teach baboons to use pen and paper have resulted at best in wild scrawling, but usually only in the destruction of the materials. It is likely that the Egyptians really did use baboons to turn irrigation treadmills, probably while the animals were chained in position and urged on by occasional blows from an overseer. It is doubtful that baboons would voluntarily net fish or dock boats alone, although there is a crab-eating macaque in India and rhesus macaques have been known to fish for minnows and eat them alive. Probably baboons could be made to perform such tasks under supervision. Baboons can be trained to climb trees and throw down fruit and to weed fields. Most of the other tricks depicted by Egyptian artists have been duplicated by modern trainers and scientific researchers.

While the Egyptians exploited the baboon as cheap labor, they also enjoyed the baboon as performer, both in religious ritual and for entertainment. Of modern history's many monkey entertainers, however, relatively few have been true baboons. The French comedian Gil Maison had a monkey that could jitterbug, dress itself and pretend to conduct an orchestra while playing a toy piano, but the animal was a large rhesus macaque, not one of the larger true baboons. Gus and Casey Augspurg, who entertained in England in the 1950s, owned two baboons and several macaques. Mary Jane, their seventeen-year-old savanna baboon, and Judy, a macaque, set up their own table and chairs and conduct a "tea party" with soda pop and bananas.

But for the most part the larger baboons are conspicuously absent from the monkey acts seen on the variety stage, in circuses and on television. Obviously, a troupe of performing hamadryas or mandrills would make a stunning circus display. But baboons do not take to show business. They do not like being stared at, since a direct stare is a challenge in baboon society. And unlike the compliant chimpanzees, most baboons will not tolerate being laughed at. They have quick tempers and even the females are large enough to pose a potential danger to trainers and, more important, to the audience. Although the Egyptians probably trained males, there is no modern record of any adult male baboon ever having been induced to cavort for the public amusement.

On the other hand, baboons submit with surprising readiness to relationships with men in which they enjoy comparative freedom, and they will often willingly perform tasks which do not subject them to ridicule or unreasonable restraint.

In the days before European settlement of Bechuanaland, baboons were reportedly kept as slaves. They were taught to lead oxen and were said to have learned the commands for stop, trot, slow and turn left or right. It was said that wild baboons would locate and dig for underground water in times of drought. So baboon slaves were denied water until they were very thirsty, then were led out on chains to locate water for their human masters. African farmers use captive baboons as water diviners in the same way today.

Also, according to popular historians, baboons

made particularly good herdsmen, and often no force was necessary to teach them the work. They were given complete command of the flocks, even learning to protect the lambs from attacks by wild baboons. Some baboon herdsmen became too protective, driving their flocks back to the field if they so much as suspected there might be a wild troop in the area.

Only a few years ago, a newspaper reported that in Okahandja, South West Africa, a female baboon named Ahla took over complete supervision of a large herd of goats. Each morning, Ahla would climb aboard the biggest billy goat and lead the column out to pasture. She was a strict disciplinarian, allowing no lingering or straying, but she was also affectionate, grooming her horned charges at every opportunity. She knew each member of the herd by sight and always made sure that they all got back to the fold at night. And she learned it all without human guidance, probably taking many of her cues from the goats themselves. Undoubtedly the most famous trained baboon in history was the amazing Jackie, railroading's only recorded baboon switchman.

Jackie was a large male chacma belonging to James Edwin Wide, who in 1890 was railroad switchman at Uitenhage, Cape of Good Hope province. Wide had lost both legs in an accident and had to hobble around on a pair of peg legs. But he had Jackie. There were six vertical steel switches at the Uitenhage station, and Wide taught the baboon their names and how to use them. He had only to call out the name of one of the switches, and Jackie would go to it, unlock it and throw the switch. The switches were nearly five feet tall, but Jackie stood four and a half feet and was very powerful. After the train had passed, the baboon would throw the switch back and lock it again.

Jackie also pushed the crippled Wide to and from work on a handcar, climbing aboard for the downhill parts of the journey. On Saturday nights, the baboon accompanied Wide to the tavern, where he would carry trays of drinks from the bar to the table, always putting his own drink aside before distributing the rest. He also helped Wide in the garden, carrying off trash and bringing tools. He pumped the water. And before Wide left the house, the faithful baboon would brush him off with a whisk broom.

Railroad officials were unaware that they had a baboon as an assistant switchman until the day that Wide fell ill on the job. That evening the oncoming express train whistled four times, the signal to open the switches. Jackie heard it and shook his master awake, but Wide could not move from his cot. Jackie got the keys from the hook on the wall, picked up a lantern and stepped out of the little signal shack. First he turned a handle operating a signal three-quarters of a mile away, giving the express the all-clear. Then he unlocked the correct switch and threw it open. As the express roared by, the engineer looked down and saw a baboon standing beside the rails with a lantern, waving him on his way.

A few months later, Jackie made the mistake of threatening a railroad employee who had been tormenting him. The man returned a few days later, when Wide was elsewhere, crept up behind Jackie and struck him dead with an iron crowbar.

Not many baboons have been kept as pets outside of Africa. It is one thing to allow a baboon the run of a large South African farmyard, it is quite another to keep a baboon in the confines of a city home. Nonetheless, a few have tried it. One of them is a California sculptress named Julie Macdonald, who for two years kept a young female hamadryas named Abu. In her book *Almost Human*, Mrs. Macdonald says that the experience was one of the most rewarding of her life, but also one of the most heart-breaking.

At two and a half years of age, Abu was a bundle of irrepressible energy and boundless affection. Although she had been born in the wilds and had lived her first year with her natural mother and troop, she quickly adopted Julie Macdonald as her mother and Mrs. Macdonald's family and friends as her troop. She groomed them all and soon had them grooming her in return—parting or pushing aside the hair with the left hand and picking delicately at the skin with the tips or the nails of the fingers of the right hand, all the time smacking the lips and now and then uttering a satisfied grunt. Abu also groomed the cat Sam, the great Dane Ludwig, and several other of the household pets, including a pygmy marmoset.

From the beginning, Abu had a very good sense of dominance. She knew exactly where each member of the household stood in the pecking order, and when she felt threatened by one of the Macdonald children she would usually run to Mrs. Macdonald, who was obviously head of the troop, and present to her. She would greet all strangers in the traditional baboon manner, sniffing them, presenting to them, smacking her lips and perhaps raising her arm to indicate that she wouldn't mind being groomed. She liked best to be groomed in the armpit.

She had the baboon's profound need for companionship. Left alone in her room, she would stand on her head and scream, while her hair bristled and her seat pads turned bright red. Once, when her mistress failed to rise at the usual hour, she tossed all her toys, one by one, at Mrs. Macdonald's bedroom door. She had good aim, frequently played handball by herself and was fond of watching football on TV. Almost every morning she greeted the rising sun with a shrill bark, and she often barked when the sun came out from behind the clouds.

Over a period of about two years, Julie Macdonald learned from Abu how to speak passable baboonese

and was later able to use some of the sounds successfully with zoo baboons. One of the sounds she reports was a very soft, low whirring, delivered while Abu
looked long and deeply into her eyes. Mrs. Macdonald
felt that the sound was an expression of strong emo-
tions, but could offer no further explanation. Abu in
her turn learned to understand her own name and
these words in English: no, good girl, bad girl,
Mammy, Judy, Alex, sit, lie down, stop, cut it out,
come here, get off the table, get on your chair, on your
pot, on your blanket, get your doll, baby, don't touch,
let's go for a ride, drink your milk, get the kitty. No
accompanying gestures were needed to get the little baboon to make the proper responses. However, she only
sat on her pot to please Mrs. Macdonald and never
consented to be completely toilet-trained.

Abu came into estrus early and was mated with a
young male hamadryas named Amon from the San
Diego zoo. After the honeymoon was over, Amon began to show signs of hostility toward his bride. It was
thought that he might be less touchy in his own territory, so the couple was accordingly moved to the zoo
in the spring of 1963. A few months later, Julie Macdonald received word that Abu had died of exhaustion
and probably also of bites inflicted by Amon.

Perhaps Amon had been defending his territory,
and certainly all male baboons need more than one
mate. But it is also possible that Abu's having been

raised among humans had left her unprepared for life with other baboons.

Of the world's captive baboons, most are in zoos. Today there are about five hundred baboons in American zoos and probably three times that number in zoos elsewhere. Most of them are savanna baboons, although the hamadryas and the many-hued mandrill are the most popular with the public. The gelada is relatively rare in zoos.

Baboons are also kept captive for scientific, industrial and medical research. The Russians have maintained a large colony of baboons at Sukhumi in their state of Georgia since 1927. The Southwest Foundation for Research and Education in San Antonio, Texas, maintains the largest colony in the United States, comprising around nine hundred savanna baboons from Kenya, where the Foundation maintains a year-round laboratory and trapping station on land donated by Kenya's government. There are also baboons in the primate colony at Holloman Air Force Base in New Mexico, and baboons are kept by numerous other medical and research facilities throughout the United States. For many years the rhesus macaque was the most popular monkey for medical research, but the larger savanna baboon is more and more favored by researchers investigating some types of body functions and diseases of man. Baboons are physiologically similar to man in many ways. Although they have a higher metabolic rate, their central nervous system is similar to man's. Most of their internal organs are similar, and the pancreas is nearly identical. Surgeons find the baboon's larger size convenient. As one doctor has said, "The animal has arteries you can grab hold of and its organs are large enough to be found without much difficulty."

Unlike the rhesus, the baboon does not easily catch certain of man's viruses, such as influenza. On the other hand, researchers find it helpful that the baboon is susceptible to many of man's more serious diseases, including various fungi, cancer, arteriosclerosis, measles and polio. Baboons are presently being used for research in heart disease, thyroid disease, embryology, neurophysiology and ovarian physiology. Baboons are also used for research and surgeon training in open-heart surgery and heart transplants. Baboon lungs and kidneys have been autografted, that is, removed, frozen overnight, then replaced. Someday it may be common surgical practice to transplant baboon kidneys into the bodies of humans. Captive baboons are also proving useful to industry, to the aerospace agencies and the military, and to the natural sciences.

The drug industry makes increasing use of baboons for testing their products. When malformed babies were born to hundreds of Scandinavian women who had taken the drug thalidomide while pregnant, the drug was given to pregnant female baboons, with similar results. Had it been tested on baboons before its release for public use, the tragic consequences might have been avoided.

Baboons have been taught to smoke, both by tobacco companies seeking to prove that cigarette smoking does not cause cancer and by agencies seeking to prove that it does. Three baboons at the Louisiana State University School of Medicine have been smoking heavily for a year while scientists check daily to see if they have developed hardening of the arteries.

The Ford Motor Company has sponsored experiments at Holloman Air Force Base, using baboons as high-speed crash victims to test new safety devices. It was from nearby White Sands that the first rhesus macaque was recovered alive from a nose cone after a rocket flight in 1951. Ten years later the chimp Ham survived a ballistics rocket flight, clearing the way for the first man in space. In 1969, a pig-tailed macaque named Bonny was blasted into orbit from Cape Kennedy to begin the longest space journey ever undertaken by a living creature. The animal died before it had completed its thirty-day flight, but its death contributed new clues to a rapid dehydration which seems to take place in living tissue during prolonged space flight.

Many of the experiments at the Holloman Air Force Base are for the National Aeronautics and Space

Smoking baboon, part of Louisiana State University experiment

Administration (NASA) and are designed to study the hazards of space flight. Animals are strapped to sleds and shot down a track at high speeds to provide experimenters with information on the effects of deceleration and violent impact.

Other government agencies make use of the Holloman facilities as well. Under the guidance of the Bureau of Narcotics, monkeys are taught to inject themselves with addictive chemical compounds so that Bureau scientists may study the results.

At any given time there are probably around three thousand baboons being used for research throughout the world, with about half that number "sacrificed,"

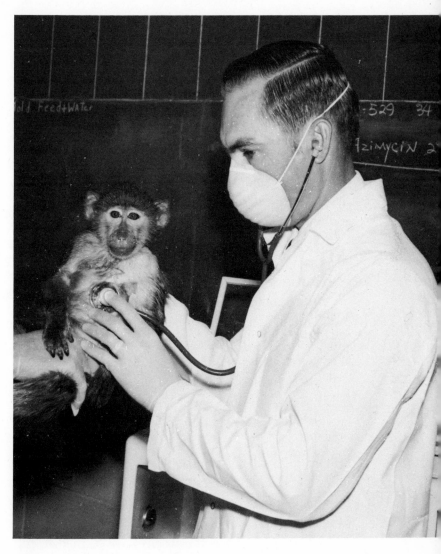

Checkup in the nursery at the Southwest Foundation

that is, killed in the course of research operations each year. Certainly some of this experimentation is wasteful and redundant, but there can be no doubt that much of it will result in benefits for all of us. According to one researcher, if baboons had been used instead of rabbits and mice, a vaccine for polio might have been developed fifty years earlier than it was.

Other Air Force experiments have included conditioning response tests designed to study the comparative learning abilities of the chimpanzee, the gibbon and the baboon.

There are many ways to measure intelligence or adaptive responses. The purpose of the Holloman experiments was to determine which of the three species of primate could best be conditioned or trained to perform certain tasks while orbiting the earth in a space vehicle. Each animal was chained in front of a panel of keys and levers. For some tasks, the animal was cued with the sounding of a particular electronic tone. If it failed to push the appropriate key or lever within a certain period of time, it received an electric shock.

The animals were scored on how quickly they learned to avoid the pain of the electric shock by performing the tasks correctly. The chimpanzees learned the quickest, the baboons were next and the gibbons were the slowest.

In other experiments baboons have learned to follow mazes, use levers and remove padlocks. They have learned to use rakes and strings to obtain food, and to push a box into proper position, climb onto it and reach for food suspended from the ceiling.

South African farmers have long insisted that baboons can count to two but not to three or above. However, in the laboratory a young baboon named Cowboy has been taught to count to five. He has learned to first push a button and turn on a light, the color of which indicates how many electronic beeps he must wait for before pushing another button that returns him a food pellet. When the red light comes on, he waits for only one beep before pushing the food button; but when the blue light comes on, he counts five beeps before pushing the button. Researchers hope eventually to teach Cowboy to add.

Another way to measure intelligence is to compare accomplishments of the species. Of all the evolutionary advances that give man advantage over the baboon and the other primates, the most important are bipedalism, hunting, the invention of tools and the invention of a spoken language. As we have seen, baboons have taken the first steps toward development of all four skills. Baboons frequently stand upright for brief periods of time. They have learned to hunt, kill and eat flesh. They appear to make rudimentary use of tools and weapons. And they have a language of vocal and other signals which may be vastly more expressive and complicated than we know at the present time.

Abu, female hamadryas raised by Julie Macdonald

In many ways the baboon is still a mystery and there are many things still to learn about its behavior. At this moment there are skilled men and women watching him in arid desert, rocky upland and dense forest, and their findings are certain to contradict some of the statements and conclusions of this book. We have done our best to tell what is known and concluded so far, leaving the door open as wide as possible for the new and perhaps surprising revelations that are sure to come. We can repeat with confidence that mankind has much in common with the baboon. We are physiologically similar to the baboon in certain important and, to us, useful ways. Like the baboon, we are primates who long ago left the trees to take up a more difficult and challenging life in the open. Like the baboon, we have evolved into a highly social, aggressive and venturesome animal, with all the advantages and difficulties that such evolution brings.

The baboon has had an important place in man's history. Will he be a part of man's future? At the same time that there are men studying the baboon in laboratory and field, there are many others invading his habitat and even setting out deliberately to destroy him. The Ethiopian government recently gave permission to several hundred people to move into the rocky highlands that constitute the gelada's last free range. The same highlands also constitute the last refuge of the Ethiopian ibex, a nearly extinct species. At this moment the homesteaders are burning off the grazing and killing off the game, ibex and baboon alike. Attempts by Peace Corps volunteers and interested wildlife organizations to have the area declared a game preserve are answered by the Ethiopian government with the undeniable truth that Ethiopia is not a rich country and that its people are hungry and must be fed. It is not a problem with an easy solution, and it is only one among many.

Certainly the baboon is not one of the most endangered species; many millions of baboons still survive in Africa. But we would do well to recall that some twenty million buffalo once roamed the North American continent, and that they were virtually wiped out in a decade. Man can be a determined exterminator, and there are many men in Africa today who would like to see the baboon eliminated entirely.

If the governments of Africa are to be persuaded not to sell off that continent's great animal parks piecemeal in order to feed their hungry peoples, then the feeding of those people as well as the preservation of the parks must soon become an international objective. Otherwise, the baboon and his marvelous world will disappear, along with much of the other wildlife of this earth, probably before the turn of the century. And we are only just now, and perhaps too late, beginning to realize that for every species we destroy, for every interference with the earth's complex natural system, we pay eventually in pollution, pestilence and aberration. The baboon, along with every other living thing, is a part of that system which we must learn to understand and control with reason, lest we disrupt it entirely and destroy ourselves in the process.

APPENDIX

BABOON COMMUNICATION

Description	Class of Animal	Situation
THREAT AND ATTACK		
Single bark: part bark, part snarl, part howl; delivered with mouth wide open on middle sound, lips drawn back against teeth: *arr-AH-hoo*.	Any adult	Expression of sudden alarm; startle or warning sound, usually prompted by sight of danger. Also during in-troop squabbling. Also at sunrise when sun comes out from behind clouds.
Double or two-phase bark: audible for over ½ mile in mountainous districts, often repeated about 1 per 2–5 seconds: *arr-AH-hoo-AH-hoo*.	Adult males	Warning bark of dominant males, in reaction to presence of humans or other predators. Also threat between males and threat toward young males, females, juveniles.

BABOON COMMUNICATION (continued)

Description	Class of Animal	Situation
Yawning, staring, eyelid blinking, ear flattening, teeth grinding, rocking body forward and back, slapping or scraping ground with hand, hand flicking, snatching and throwing branches and stones. Often accompanied by grunting.	Any adult	Gamut of *threat behavior* toward predator or another baboon, can cease at any point or lead to actual attack.
Grunting: soft, sometimes two-phase, delivered with jaw dropped slightly, lips closed or nearly closed; ½ second for each sound: *uh-huh, uh-huh.*	Adult males	Prelude to mild threat gestures toward another animal, can escalate into threatening roar. Can also indicate pleasure (see page 145, FRIENDLY).
Roaring: loud two-phase grunting, escalating into crescendo of loud grunts: *unh-unh-unh-unh.*	Adult males	Ultimate threat behavior, occurs during attacks on predators and men and during serious fights between adult males.

FEAR AND ESCAPE

Description	Class of Animal	Situation
Screech: high-pitched, usually repeated; similar to human screech of fright.	Any animal	In fear or terror; often by females, subadult males or juveniles when fleeing from dominant male.
Fear grimace: shrinks back, ears flat against head, eyes starting, lips retracted from clenched teeth. Often accompanied by yakking.	Any animal	In fear; often by females or subadult males threatened by dominant male or other danger.

BABOON COMMUNICATION (continued)

Description	Class of Animal	Situation
Yakking: single sharp sound, repeated 2 or 3 times: *gekkeh, gekkeh, gekkeh*.	Any adult or subadult	When animal withdraws from threat, usually from dominant male or outside danger. Accompanies fear grimace.
Chirplike clicking: progressively rising in pitch and volume: *quek-quek-quek*.	Infant and juvenile	Often preliminary to temper tantrum, probably juvenile equivalent of yakking.
Ick-ooer: repeated sharp *ick*-sound followed by longer *ooer*-sound; or merely: *ehck-ehck-ehck* or *kek-kek-kek*.	Infants, occasionally juveniles	Frustration and protest against pain, discomfort, usually minor. Accompanied by twitching of head, shoulders and arms, and by grinning.

FRIENDLY

Description	Class of Animal	Situation
Lip-smacking: rapid, with tongue protruding slightly between compressed lips: *tschp, tschp, tschp*.	Any animal	Pacification, greeting, often accompanies grooming and presenting.
Grunting: varies in frequency from slow, about 1 per 2 seconds, to very rapid: *unh-unh-unh*. With juveniles can be nasal, more rapid: *chattering*. Can also be a "chorus" throughout the troop.	Any animal or all animals, except possibly infants	Heard at intervals during feeding, courting, greeting, also at night; often heard in chorus of whole troop, particularly near sleeping place at nightfall.
Gurgle: 1–2 seconds for each sound, quavering with increased volume: *oah-oah-oah*.	Infants and juveniles, possibly adults	Extreme pleasure, heard when separated animals reunited, and during mating.

BABOON COMMUNICATION (continued)

Description	Class of Animal	Situation
Giggle: mouth slightly open, teeth partly exposed: *heh-heh-heh*. Rising volume, becomes laugh.	Infants, juveniles, possibly adults	Heard in play and teasing, when infant tickled in ribs.

UNCLASSIFIED

Description	Class of Animal	Situation
Moaning: finale to temper tantrum, similar to human anguish sound: *aohh-aohh-aohh*.	Juveniles, probably adults	Heard from Abu by owner Julie Macdonald. Might also be sound of mourning the dead heard by Eugène Marais.
Whirring: softly, deep in throat, faces close together, eyes in deep and penetrating stare: *Whrrrrrrrrrrrrrr*.	Juveniles, possibly adults	Heard from Abu by owner Julie Macdonald, usually after lip-smacking. Intense emotion, meaning unknown.

BIBLIOGRAPHY

AMERICAN SOCIETY OF MAMMOLOGISTS. *Recent Mammals of the World.* Sydney Anderson, J. K. Jones, et al., contributors. New York: Ronald Press, 1967.

ARDREY, ROBERT. *African Genesis.* New York: Atheneum, 1961.

CARPENTER, C. R. *Naturalistic Behavior of Nonhuman Primates.* University Park: Pennsylvania State University Press, 1964.

CARRIGHAR, SALLY. *Wild Heritage.* Boston: Houghton-Mifflin, 1965.

CLARK, W. E. LE GROS. *History of the Primates.* Chicago: University of Chicago Press, 1965.

COPELAND, G. H., "Good in the Bad Baboon." *New York Times Magazine,* September 25, 1960.

DEVORE, IRVEN, ed. *Primate Behavior.* New York: Holt, 1965.

DEVORE, IRVEN, and SAREL EIMERL. *Primates.* New York: Time-Life, 1965.

DEVORE, IRVEN, and S. L. WASHBURN. "Social Life of Baboons." *Scientific American,* June, 1961.

DRIMMER, FREDERICK, ed. *The Animal Kingdom.* 3 vols. New York: Greystone Press, 1954.

GOODRICH, S. G. *The Illustrated Natural History of the Animal Kingdom*. Vol. 1. New York: Derby and Jackson, 1861.

HEGNER, ROBERT, and JANE (ZABRISKIE). *Parade of the Animal Kingdom*. New York: Macmillan, 1935.

HUXLEY, THOMAS H. *Man's Place in Nature*. 1863. Reprint. Ann Arbor: University of Michigan Press, 1959.

INTERNATIONAL SYMPOSIUM ON THE BABOON AND ITS USE AS AN EXPERIMENTAL ANIMAL—BABOON IN MEDICAL RESEARCH. Proceedings, edited by Harold Vagtborg. Austin: University of Texas Press, 1967.

LE GROS CLARK, W. E. *See* CLARK, W. E. LE GROS.

MACDONALD, JULIE. *Almost Human*. New York: Chilton, 1965.

MANNIX, DANIEL P. "The Bewildering Baboon." *Holiday* 31: 29–35 (March, 1962).

MARAIS, EUGÈNE N. *My Friends the Baboons*. New York: McBride, 1949. Published under the title *The Soul of the Ape*. New York: Atheneum, 1969.

MORRIS, DESMOND. *Mammals*. New York: Harper & Row, 1965.

———. *The Naked Ape*. New York: McGraw-Hill, 1967.

MORRIS, DESMOND and RAMONA. *Men and Apes*. New York: McGraw-Hill, 1966.

PFEIFFER, JOHN E. "The Apish Origins of Human Tension." *Harper's* 227:55–60 (July, 1963).

SANDERSON, IVAN. *The Monkey Kingdom*. Garden City, N.Y.: Hanover House, 1958.

SCOTT, JOHN PAUL. *Animal Behavior*. Chicago: University of Chicago Press, 1958.

SPINAGE, CLIVE A. *Animals of East Africa*. Boston: Houghton-Mifflin, 1963.

VAGTBORG, HAROLD. *See* INTERNATIONAL SYMPOSIUM ON THE BABOON.

ZUCKERMAN, SOLLY. *The Social Life of Monkeys and Apes*. London: Routledge & Kegan Paul, 1932.

INDEX